MY

RHYMES

AND

RAMBLINGS

MY RHYMES AND RAMBLINGS

By

Danny McFaul

Formatted using Microsoft Word

Printed and bound in the United Kingdom.

ISBN 978-1-4477-9825-5

Also By Danny Mc Faul

Dan Mc Faul the Weaver

ISBN 937184426994

The Shame of the Workhouse

My Rhymes & Ramblings

ISBN 978-1-4477-9825-5

Contents

A Selection of short stories

A Selection of children's stories

A Selection of Rhymes

How We Lived During the War

A

Selection

Of

Short

Stories

A drop of the Hard Stuff

Bellaghy is one of the most talked about villages in the County of Antrim with its two traditional pubs and cafes surrounding the village green and the duck pond near to where the old stocks used to be situated in the 1700s. This is where wrongdoers were securely fastened to repent for their misdeeds. The village from the east is overlooked by the Spire from St. Patrick's church which dates from the fifteenth century and has some of the oldest surviving archaeology in the country. To the west is one of the oldest Limestone Mills in the Country. The village was infected by Cholera in 1854 when it claimed the lives of many victims. Popular belief is that it was brought there by a woman lodger from Glenkey who had come to the village for a Fair Day. The local men spread limestone from the mill in the streets to try to stem the outbreak. The old mill is now a museum showing how life used to be in Bellaghy and the surrounding area. Young Kevin Flynn loved Bellaghy. His Grandparents had lived there in a Rose covered cottage and he remembered with great affection the times when he came to visit when he was a boy. For two weeks every summer he would stay with his Grandparents. His Grandfather was the local blacksmith, as was his father before him and he knew almost everyone in the village. Those that his Grandfather didn't know his Grandmother did. Kevin looked forward to that fortnight more than he did Christmas or any other time. His parents would take him to the village by train from Ballyrea where they lived. Then having seen his parents off in the afternoon, Kevin and his Grandfather would walk back to the cottage past the old mill. At that time just before the Second World War, they called it the old mill, even though it had been quite a few years since it had been in working order. Kevin would spend his time walking in the woods with his Grandfather or his Grandmother, or feeding the ducks on the pond and playing games on the green with the local children. When the time came for Kevin to return home his father and mother would arrive in the early afternoon and Kevin would go home with them on the next train dreaming about his next trip. Kevin was about ten years old when war broke out. His mother would pack him and his Gasmask off to stay with his Grandparents because she thought it would be safer in the country than it would be in the town and of course she was right. Not only was it safer, but it was great fun too. A few miles away at Ralston Aerodrome was home to many members of the American Air Force during the early 1940s. These troops were there for training, prior to the invasion of North Africa. Kevin used to sit and watch the bombers and Dakotas fly in and out of the base. He would count them out and then back in and report any losses to his Grandparents. He also got to know the sounds of the different planes and he could recognise if any of them were enemy planes. One Christmas brought some excitement as over a dozen heavy bombers were forced to land just outside the village because the Aerodrome was covered in thick fog. The Americans were good for the local economy. The shops and the pubs were never so busy and some had to take on new staff at busy weekends. The Americans had plenty of money to spend and were, to be fair, quite generous. Kevin and the other village children learnt early on that if they kept friendly with the Americans they'd never be short of chewing gum or chocolate and the odd penny or even tuppence and judging by the number of local girls that were now wearing nylon stockings in the village the children weren't the only ones who were being friendly. The forge where Kevin's grandfather worked was the central focal point of village life for centuries. It was a meeting place for men and boys, almost like a 'men's club', where news was exchanged and the politics of the day discussed. The blacksmith was a mine of information on local family history and news from around the country, carried by travellers who often called at his door in need of his expert help. The forge was dimly lit and medium-sized. There was no machinery as such, the blacksmith made his own tools, consisting of an anvil, which in the early days may have been a rough piece of iron ore, a vice, bellows turned by a hand crank, tongs, rake and poker for the fire and an assortment of welding and Horse Shoeing tools. Kevin would assist his Grandfather by making sure that the fire was well stoked. It was set on a raised hearth made from five or six flagstones. Charcoal, turf, coke, peat and coal were all used, depending upon local availability. The forge was quite near to the Duck pond which was very handy for cooling purposes. Mending wheels was one of the blacksmith's important jobs. Many a traveller was pleased to see the Blacksmith as they limped into the village minus a shoe for the Horse or a fractured wheel for the cart. A strip of iron was cut, shaped and welded together, just a little smaller than the wheel. A circular fire was mad of peat on the ground outside the forge and the iron band placed in it. When red hot, it was taken up with tongs and placed upon the wooden wheel, where it was quickly hammered into place whilst buckets of water were poured over it from the pond to prevent the wheel from catching fire. The blacksmith produced all the tools needed to farm and all the tools needed in the community such as pots and pans, knives and forks. A Blacksmith like Kevin's Great Grandfather about a hundred years earlier; could make many different items, including weapons for hunting and warfare. The Blacksmith's trade was usually hereditary, often tracing back five or six generations. The blacksmith 'knew' horses, and could cure ailments such as Pharsey or Strangles. He would treat sores and sprains with washes made from water from the cooling trough. He pulled horses' teeth with specially made forceps, and 'bled' horses with an instrument called a Fleam. The Blacksmith also acted as dentist to the human population. He would tie a piece of string to the afflicted tooth and attached the other end to the heavy anvil.

With the   sudden presentation of a hot iron to the sufferer's face, the tooth was pulled as the "patient" pulled their head back from the red hot poker. Trough water was said to cure many ailments, especially skin disorders such as warts and boils. Cuts and sprains were dipped into the trough, and the water could be bottled and taken to the patient. It was said that a squint could be cured by applying trough water to the eyes for three days running. Many small mending jobs were done by the Blacksmith in exchange for food from local farmers. He worked all day with iron, which was believed to protection against evil. He was also believed to be able to lay good charms and spells, and a liberal sprinkling of forge water was said to undo any evil against land, milk, hens or pigs. There were two pubs in the village of Bellaghy the Duck and Drake and the Green Man and they faced each other across the village green. The landlord of the Duck & Drake was Shamus Magill, a chubby, red-faced man in his late fifties. His wife Kathleen helped out behind the bar and cooked lovely home-made meals that became famous amongst the Americans at Ralston. There was a saying in those days that "You never tasted County Antrim food until you'd sampled it at the Duck & Drake". That was the message to any new airmen arriving at the base. The most popular dish on the pub menu was Kathleen's Irish Mix which was potatoes and as it was War Rations that were used, whatever else was available at the time. The airmen loved it and the pub always seemed to have enough supplies to keep something interesting on the menu. Young Kevin and his friends had a theory that the airmen were bringing back livestock and vegetables during their bombing raids over Europe. The Green Man on the other hand specialised in local ales rather than food. Patrick O'Hara was the landlord. His wife Mary had died a few years before the war started and he ran the pub mostly to keep himself busy. Of the two pubs, Patrick's only attracted a few loyal locals, and sometimes Patrick would shut early, if there weren't many customers and he and his remaining customers would go and join Shamus and Kathleen at the Duck & Drake. That was the spirit of the village of Patrick would now and then end up helping out behind the bar if necessary in his "Rival's" pub. Young Kevin would often accompany his grandfather to the Duck & Drake and spend the evening sipping his lemonade and listening to the many stories that the older people in the village were famous for and indeed many other villages in the County. The American airmen were also very good at telling tales of their latest adventures; though young Kevin thought that most of them were like film stories. After the war had finished Kevin went back to live with his parents. He was twenty-one when he next visited the village. It wasn't a happy occasion, as his Grandmother had been taken ill and died quite suddenly. Kevin and his mother and father attended the funeral in the Church of St. Patrick. On the way back from the church his Grandfather said to him, "Tell you what young Kevin let's go over to the Duck & Drake. In all the years you've been coming here, I've never bought you a beer. Now you're old enough, I reckon we should go and remember the good times we used to have". Kevin turned round to his parents to make sure that it would be okay and his mother nodded. The Duck & Drake was a lot quieter now Kevin noticed. Shamus Magill was still behind the bar, his red face still as round as Kevin remembered it. He nodded to Kevin's Grandfather and muttered a few words of condolence. Then he saw Kevin. "Bless my soul" he said. "It can't be young Kevin can it we haven't seen you for ages". Kevin grinned, he was surprised at how many of the locals still remembered him, and how many of the old faces that he had recognised at the church service. He'd spent a lot of the day listening to everyone telling him how much he'd grown since they last seen him. He had replied that they still looked the same as ever. Come to think of it most of them did. "He works in the big city" said Kevin's Grandfather. "He hasn't got time for the likes of us Country Bumpkins". He smiled at Kevin and gave him a little nudge. "He's right" replied Kevin, "I should make some time to come here more often".

"You should" said Shamus.

"So what do you do that keeps you so busy"?

"I'm a reporter I work for a paper in Belfast, boring stuff mostly local court cases, the odd football match all small stuff really".

"Sounds interesting" said Shamus.

"It pays the bills. I'm still waiting for a big scoop. Now what about that Drink"?

"I still have some lemonade if you want it" Shamus said.

"But I dare say now that you are old enough you will want to try some of the hard stuff".

'That's right Shamus" said Kevin's Grandfather.

"It's the first time I've had a chance to sit and have a proper drink with him, so two pints of whatever you've got on today".

"It's on the house" said Shamus putting two pints of beer on the bar "Seeing as I couldn't make the service for your Grandmother". Kevin and his grandfather raised their glasses to the Landlord and then they went and sat at a table by the window. "I've been wondering lately" began the old man, "If I used to spend too much time in here and not enough time with your Grandmother". "She was probably glad to get you out of the house from under her feet most times" said Kevin smiling as his grandfather laughed. "You're probably right son. She had more time that way to gossip with the locals".

"Talking of which, where are they"

"Who"?

"All the customers this place used to be packed from what I can remember".

"Most of them go to the Green Man now" said his Grandfather.

"The Green Man, why is that"? The old man looked out of the window at the other pub.

"I guess the beer tastes better. Most of the Locals go in there now. It's become quite popular since old Patrick sold up".

"He sold it" said Kevin. "Who to"?

"Well, after the War had finished a lot of the yanks moved from the Aerodrome into the village. As well as the Americans there were also a couple of new families that moved in as well, and one of them bought the Green Man from Patrick".

"New families you say"?

"Yes they came from the South somewhere, Galway I think".

"Oh right, do they serve some foreign beer then" Kevin said jokingly. "I haven't been in there. I've seen the landlord in the shop now and again, but I like the Duck & Drake and to be honest, it's nice and quiet in here, I prefer it that way". Kevin smiled at his Grandfather.

"It does have a certain charm, talking of which, I'm hungry". Kevin said as he turned round to the bar.

"Mr Magill" he called.

"Shamus, if you please young Kevin" Said Shamus.

"Okay. Shamus, does your good lady still do that Irish Mix"?

"I'm sure she can manage to rustle up something," he said, disappearing through the door that led to the kitchen. Kevin made several more visits to see his Grandfather over the next five years or so. His final visit was to the Church of St. Patrick, to attend his dear grandfather's funeral. The church was packed with local people for the service. Kevin's Grandfather had been a popular figure in the village and was well liked. He was astonished to see that most of the villagers that he remembered from his time here during the war still looked the same. In fact most of them now looked about the same age as his parents. But by rights, thought Kevin, some of them should be dead.

"He was a good man" said a voice that snapped Kevin back to reality. He looked up.

"Oh hello Mr O'Neill said Kevin.

'Thank you yes he was. Are you going to come back to the house later for a drink"?

"No I won't if you don't mind. I'm not as young as I once was and I must be getting back". Kevin was reminded of what he was thinking earlier and looked at the old man before him. He remembered how his grandfather had spoken of 'old O'Neill' and of seeing the old man going for his Sunday papers. He had always figured that Mr O'Neill was older than his Grandfather, but he must have been mistaken. The figure in front of him looked about the same age no, younger than he remembered him but how was that possible.

"Are you all right boy"? Mr O'Neill asked.

"What oh sorry Mr O'Neill it's been a long day"? Kevin said.

"Yes it has, not easy to say goodbye to an old friend"

"No it isn't, thanks again" replied Kevin. Mr O'Neill walked off. Not an old man's walk stiff with arthritis thought Kevin, but a firm stride of someone a lot younger than Mr O'Neill actually is. Kevin looked around at the other guests. None of the older people were stooped over, limping or shuffling like you'd expect of people that at the least were approaching their eighties. Kevin made his way back to his Grandfather's house. His parents were already there his mother was laying out some sandwiches and cakes for the people that had been at the service.

"Hello Kevin; are you okay son"?

"Yes thank you Mum" he answered.

He looked at his mother. She was sixty years old, and looked older than many of the people that were even older than his Grandfather.

"Mum"? Kevin said. His mother looked up from the pile of fairy cakes that she was making..

"Have you noticed all the old people"? Kevin said.

"What old people"? His mother asked.

"Well, look at Sybil Armstrong from the Post Office. How old would you say that she is?"

His mother's lips moved as she counted silently.

"Oh, I don't know" she said.

"Seventy maybe even Seventy five"?

"At least, she must've been past retirement when I was here during the war. That was over fifteen years ago. Look at her". Kevin and his mother looked into the garden where old Sybil was walking around chatting to some of the other villagers. At one point she bent to pick something from the ground.

"Look", said Kevin.

"She didn't event creak".

"It must be the country air. They don't get that horrible smog that we get in the towns and cities. Everyone is much healthier in the country with fresh fruit and vegetables and fresh meat. What else could it be"?

"I don't know, it's just weird, that's all" said Kevin.

"It's just that you remember it as it was when you were young". His mother answered. Kevin shrugged and looked out of the window. From here he could see the village green and the duck pond where he and the other children used to play. The other children, Where were they. He realised that he hadn't seen any of the people he used to play with. They were all grown up now and left the village to find work he supposed. He looked at the village green. It was empty except for a few ducks taking a rest from their swimming. Where were the children, he hadn't seen any in the village at all. In fact the only people he remembered seeing in the village that were less than retirement age were the day-trippers to the Glens of Antrim. "It's a nice place to retire" his mother said. "And I don't expect that there is much work for the likes of you younger ones so I imagine that most of them move out to find decent jobs. There's no great mystery".

"Yes you're probably right and it is a nice place to retire".

When he came to retirement age Kevin remembered his youth and returned again to Bellaghy. He and his wife Margaret bought a small cottage near to the Church of St Patrick. "What's the matter"? Margaret whispered. She nudged him. "Kevin"? She whispered; they had gone to the Sunday service at the church. Kevin was staring across the pews his eyes fixed and his mouth open. "It can't be,' he said. "It can't be".

"Can't be what"?

"Old Mr O'Neill he can't be still alive, he can't be"?

"Well, quite plainly he is" whispered Margaret.

When the service had finished Kevin and Margaret were on their way out of the church when the man that Kevin had been staring at approached them.

"It's you is it not"? The old man said to Kevin.

"Kevin Flynn old Dan the Smithy's Grandson"?

"Mr O'Neill" said Kevin. O'Neill smiled and nodded. "It's nice to see you back again. It's been a few years. Why don't you come and have a drink down at the pub before lunch"? Kevin wasn't too sure, he felt as though he'd seen a ghost. He looked at Margaret. She nodded. "Go on", she said. "I'll get dinner ready while you're out. It'll be nice not to have you from under my feet for a change".

"Okay just a quick one" Kevin said. The two men wandered over to the Green Man. "I always used to go to the Duck & Drake when I was here" said Kevin.

"It's a tourist's pub now. All the locals drink in the Green Man. That's where the good beer is. Sullivan serves only the best Poteen. The tourists at the Duck & Drake get the cooking lager." Laughed old Mr O'Neill

"Sullivan"? Inquired Kevin?

"The landlord" chuckled O'Neill.

"He's from Dublin so we call him you know – Blotto". O'Neill laughed again and Kevin joined him though he didn't quite know why. Soon Mr O'Neill returned from the bar with two pints. "Sup up" he said. "It'll put a spring in your step".

It certainly tasted good Kevin thought. There was something different about it but he couldn't quite decide what.

"You're looking well" said Kevin.

"It's the Poteen" said O'Neill and winked.

"Aye lad it's the Poteen and good country air".

"I reckon you must be right. You look the same as the last time I saw you. That must be over twenty years ago".

O'Neill laughed.

"Have another pint" he said.

"You are looking well, and pleased", said Margaret when Kevin arrived home. He thought back to earlier when he had said the same thing to old M. O'Neill. "Poteen and good country air," he said, grabbing Margaret around the waist and kissing her. Margaret screamed with surprise. "I'll have to send you down there more often" she said to him. Kevin and Margaret became regulars at the Green Man and both were surprised at how active the old people in the village were. It wasn't long however before they too were feeling a lot younger than their years.

"So what's the secret then"?

Kevin asked M. O'Neill in the pub.

"I told you" replied O'Neill.

"It's the Poteen and good country air".

"Yes, I remember you saying that" said Kevin.

"It's true just look at me, I'm one hundred and seventeen years old. Sybil Armstrong over there she's one hundred and fifteen. Most of the others in here used to shop at your Grandfather's place and your Great Grandfather's shops before that. It's Sullivan's secret recipe." Kevin sat there stunned, not able to believe what he was hearing, but knowing it must be true because the evidence was there before his very eyes. "Secret recipe you say"? Kevin said. "Okay so we have a village full of old people from the forties, kept young by some secret concoction in the Beer" replied Kevin. "But what happened to all the children"?

"Ah ha, the children and he spirit of youth" said Mr O'Neill. A wicked grin came over his face. "We love children here. We find that they keep us young". As he raised his pint glass of Poteen and winked at Kevin.

Have you ever been on holiday or in a different town where you see someone that you think you know from somewhere in the past.

Is That You Frank?

As a married man my wife and I have lived in and raised our children in six different Countries during my time in the Armed Forces. My wife and family have made moving arrangements and packed and unpacked MFO boxes more times than I care to remember. But the hardest part about moving in the Army isn't the physical move it's leaving a way of life behind. Not only do you have to find your way around in a strange Regiment, in a strange country, in a strange town, you arrive there and you realize that you exist as a person without a name, because no one there knows you. For some reason, I always felt as if I needed proof of my very existence; for unless someone recognized me, how will I know if I do or not? But of course the good news about being a stranger in a new town is that you can go about your business for a while, without fear of running into someone you know like your boss. The bad news is that as time goes by you begin to search for dear old friends, even when you know that it's impossible for them to be there. My wife and I never forgot the time that I made a complete fool of myself in a Shopping Mall one busy Christmas Eve. We were making our way through the crowds when my heart started to pound. Just ahead of us, or so I thought, was an old friend from a couple of Regiments previously. "Hi, Frank," I shouted and waved, trying to get his attention. Thank goodness my eldest daughter wasn't with us or she would have said how embarrassed she was to be seen with us. Frank apparently didn't hear or see me because he just kept walking. I pushed through the crowd, mumbling excitedly about the odds of running into Frank here in Germany when the last time I had seen him was in the Sahara Desert when we were on a Military exercise there. I shouted again, this time loud enough to be heard over the Christmas Music that was blaring out all over the town. "Hi, Frank." I shouted again. The chap continued to walk on, even faster, without turning round, but I certainly got the attention of everyone else around me. I continued to push through the crowd leaving my wife to lag slightly behind, but as soon as I caught up with Frank I wished that I could shrink and crawl out of the Arcade unnoticed. "Why have you been chasing me through the Mall?" Frank asked with an irritated look on his face. (It was definitely not Frank.) "I am so sorry," I said. "I apologize, I thought I knew you." I said humbly. This sort of confusion happens to many people who are well travelled. I have many friends in my mind at times from over three continents. Apparently some small parts of our traits and our looks are fairly generic and sometimes seem to be "given" to other people. In a strange way it can be comforting, for when you meet a new person who reminds you of someone you already know, you feel like you have a touch of familiarity even if you don't; like what happened to me one day after just moving to Germany. I saw a career type woman in a tailored suit. She was quite prim and proper, with a neatly packed briefcase in one hand and purse in the other. She reminded me of a Teacher I once knew, right down to the glasses hanging on her chest from a gold plated chain. I suppose there's nothing too strange about that, except that almost every morning I noticed a tall, dark-haired man who also got on the same train. He reminded me of the Teacher's husband. They didn't get on the train together or even acknowledge that they knew each other, but I watched one morning to see if they approached the Station from the same direction. If they did know each other, they were very good at protecting their secret. I wondered if they had any idea that in another city that I know, there were near clones of their bodies living as man and wife. I was fascinated with the possibilities.

The Love of Joe's Life

Love, that's what it is, true love. Joe Boyle was walking on air. He was so high on love that he fancied the idea of jumping off a bridge just to prove that he could fly, it was tempting. Joe could see the headlines now; "Young man high on love falls to his death on take-off". But not wanting to be remembered as the person responsible for a media led Circus campaign to outlaw love, Joe opted for trying to take off from the ground instead. He ran down the road as fast as he could, his arms flapping when he thought his speed was fast enough for take-off. Two young lads who were watching him called him an idiot. Joe turned and ran towards them, tripped over a crack in a paving stone and fell crashing head first to the ground. Laughingly the two lads ran off as Joe nursed his aching head which was bleeding from a bad gash. "Damn", said Joe as he tried to stand up. But his left ankle gave way as he tried to counter the shift in his weight and he fell to the ground in a heap. Just then two young women passed by arm in arm as he nursed his ankle. "Drunken bum", one said as they passed. "I'll have you know I'm not drunk I was just trying to fly" Joe shouted in an attempt to explain what had happened. The other woman turned round, "Junkie" she called as they both hurried away giggling. Joe got up more carefully this time. His trousers were dirty and his jacket was torn as he limped off in search of a taxi. "This love business is a bit more painful than I imagined", Joe thought to himself as he put out his hand to hail an oncoming cab. Unfortunately for Joe, what the taxi driver saw was a dirty, bloodied young man, who was probably drunk; trying to throw himself in front of his cab to get chauffeured to some out of the way place miles away, where he didn't have the money to pay for the fare. This Mayfair cabby had been taxiing for long enough to know a dodgy fare when he sees one. So he opted to ignore Joe and keep on driving. Unfortunately Joe was a little too close to the taxi and the wing mirror clipped his hip sending him spinning before he fell down for the third time that evening. "None of this would have happened if I could fly Joe thought. An old man on the other side of the road saw Joe fall; he hurried across the road to see if he was okay. "Are you all right son?" Joe heard the old man say. "Are you my father?" Joe asked slightly confused at the old man's use of the word "son". The old man had the ruddy nose of a hardened drinker but his eyes were kind enough. "Don't worry I saw the whole thing that taxi could have killed you, the driver is a maniac". The old man replied disregarding Joe's question by putting it down to delirium. He leaned over Joe before saying;" That's a bad cut you have on your head, you're going to need an ambulance can you move?" To answer the old man's question Joe wiggled his fingers in the air. He was dazed and a bit confused after all he had been run over, though he didn't recall a car actually driving over him. The old man was worried that this poor soul could be concussed. Slightly unsure of what he should do he decided to ask Joe some questions just like they do on the telly. "Do you know who I am?" he asks Joe, getting the concussion diagnosis hopelessly wrong. "No... I don't think so should I, never seen you before in my life?" Joe replied his head reeling whilst thinking to himself, "Does this old drunk really think that he is my dad?" Then the old man said, "No, I know we have never met. I'm just checking if you are all right". Joe was not very happy. "Great, my rescuer has Alzheimer's. He doesn't even know who he is" Joe thought to himself, but aloud he said, "I want to go home". The old man however was having none of it. "You want to go to hospital more like", the old man replied. He knew that he would have to call for an ambulance but he didn't want to leave the injured Joe on his own. The old man's thought processes were not the fastest, but he knew that a young man like Joe probably had a mobile phone. Most of the young ones these days have mobile phones. He considered asking Joe if he had a mobile phone, but he wasn't confident that he'd get anything other than another nonsensical answer because of his patient's severe concussion. The old man began searching Joe, found a mobile phone and removed it from his pocket. "I'm being robbed by a good Samaritan with Alzheimer's" Joe thought, as he tried to struggle, but he was too weak and hurt too much. "Christ, how strong are old people supposed to be anyway?" he wondered. "What do you think you are doing?" he asked as defiantly as he could. "I'm Phoning for an ambulance, don't worry, help will be here soon", the old man assured Joe. "Hello yes emergency, ambulance please. I've got a young man here who's been run over by a suicidal taxi driver. There's a lot of blood and he seems badly confused and concussed. Yes, he's conscious. No, I won't move him. We are on the Ballymena Line near the top of the old Mill Street, that's right, don't worry. No I won't" The old man put the phone back in Joe's pocket. Joe thought that the old man was coming back to see if he had any money, or other valuables. He tried to sit up to be in a better position to defend himself from this geriatric thug. The old man pushed him down with his foot and then sat on him to stop him moving. "Are you insane?" Joe asked. "The woman on the phone says you are not to be moved." he said. "What woman, Laura?" Joe asked, thinking the old man was talking about his girlfriend, "She loves me". Joe told the old man. "She doesn't even know you". The old man said who felt that he was getting as confused as the patient. "She does, I'll tell her everything, I know she loves me". Joe insisted but he had to give up trying to talk to the old man as he couldn't move while he was sitting on him and anyway he was at the old man's mercy. A crowd was beginning to form around them and Joe didn't want to explain his predicament all over again. The whole incident had been tiring and he could feel his adrenalin levels dropping. He felt very weak and drowsy he closed his eyes for a moment and he was fast asleep. Suddenly he woke up with a start surrounded by creatures in green tunics. The bright lights in the background were hurting his eyes. "He's coming round I think, hello Sir, can you tell me who you are?" someone asked. "That was going to be my question" said Joe. "We are Paramedics Sir, do you know why we are here?" the medic asks. "Yes I do some senile mugger with an apparent nursing degree called you" Joe replied. "He's very incoherent", one green tunic said to the other, "Severe concussion looks like" and turning back to Joe he held up three fingers. "How many fingers am I holding up Sir"? Joe didn't even look at the paramedic. "Three, it's always three, don't you people ever watch the hospital dramas?" replied Joe. "Are you in any pain Sir?" the paramedic asks. "Let's see, my head hurts like hell, my ankle also hurts if I put weight on it, I'm most probably going to have a bruise the size of a football on my hip in the morning from that taxi mirror, oh and I feel really awful". Joe said. The ambulance man smiled. "You'll be fine just be a little patient and we will get you onto a stretcher and into the ambulance". "Don't you have any stretchers for big patients then?" Before Joe could begin another sarcastic remark they strapped a neck brace on him and lifted him onto the stretcher. The crowd parted and he was carried into the ambulance. On his way there, he saw the old man being interviewed by the police. "Good, they're going to arrest him", Joe murmured. Inside the hospital one of the doctors asks Joe.

"Do you know who you are?"

"Yes of course I do" replied Joe.

"Would you like to tell me please?" the doctor said smiling. "Joe Boyle" Joe replied. "Okay Joe, do you know what happened to you?" A red headed nurse leaned over Joe to clean the cut on his head as the doctor asked his questions. Joe's head was clear now and he did understand the question perfectly. "I fell in love" Joe said. "Good for you but do you know how this accident happened?" replied the doctor. "I fell in love", Joe repeated. The doctor tried to interject again but Joe held his hand up to stop the interruption as he continued. "I fell in love, tried to fly, got abused by a couple of ten year olds, tripped over a paving stone and hurt my head and ankle, got a load of verbal abuse from two women, got hit by a taxi that I was trying to hail, was mugged by an escapee from a mental home who ransacked my pockets, I fell asleep, I was woken by a couple of paramedics and now I am being interrogated by you. I think that about covers it". The doctor still not fully understanding the sequence of events and having serious concerns about Joe maybe having severe concussion asked him a few more question to get a clearer picture of what really happened. The doctor found himself laughing at Joe's extraordinary story. "That's the thing about love", the female nurse offered; "When you fall, you need your feet firmly on the ground". The doctor then told Joe "You'll be glad to know that you don't appear to be concussed to any great degree, your head wound is superficial and your ankle is just sprained. Your hip took a bit of a knock and will probably be bruised for a few days but other than that, you're going to be okay. The bad news is there are a couple of policemen outside waiting to interview you". "Could be worse, could be reporters", Joe mumbled. During his interview with the police, he was able to establish that he hadn't been robbed by the old man after all. What Joe didn't know was that the old man, a Mr Gordon Browne, was talking to a reporter about the incident. Joe's story spread though the hospital as it brought a touch of humour to a drab and reasonably busy shift. It didn't take the reporter long to get the full story from one of the porters at the hospital. The story made page two of the local Rag. Joe's girlfriend, Laura, woke up to the story being laughed at by two local radio station DJs when the radio alarm went off. She began to feel a twinge of guilt about Joe's lovesick adventure as she was at that moment, in bed with Joe's best friend.

I cannot claim to have written this story as it was sent to me some years ago by an old Army pal. I have however, put bits in bits and left bits out to make it more presentable.

Private Bradshaw.

Not many old ladies would ask their granddaughter to have a one night stand with a soldier especially if the two young people have not even been properly introduced. But that is what happened to me, in the summer of my twentieth year. It was June and I was at the end of my second year at University. I received this slightly mysterious letter from my grandmother asking me to phone her urgently. When I did phone her she invited me to go and see her. Well she more than invited me, she pretty well demanded that I go and stay with her for a couple of nights. She said that she needed my help urgently, but wouldn't elaborate on that; just said that it was a family matter and something of the utmost importance. I dearly love my Gran and I would go to quite a lot of trouble to help her and as it happened I had finished all my exams so I was able to agree to her request, though I must say I was a bit puzzled. "Bring that blue dress of yours the one with buttons up the front" Gran had said, which all added to the mystery. My grandmother lives in a small village in Yorkshire on the edge of Catterick Camp as you probably know is a centre of military activity and most of Gran's neighbours are retired Colonels or Brigadiers. The tank regiments use the area for various war games and the infantry practise street fighting in some of the deserted villages. These villages were not deserted willingly they were taken over by the army during the Second World War and have never been returned to civilian use. Gran needless to say, is heavily involved in church affairs and the village activities. She is president of the flower club, a member of the women's bowls team (despite being over eighty), and is secretary of the women's institute, or some such body. I arrived soon after lunch on a beautifully warm June day. A taxi from the nearest railway station at Richmond delivered me to Gran's door. We spent the afternoon resting, chatting, drinking tea, and calling on various neighbours. We also distributed excess vegetables from Gran's garden. "Helping the old folk" Gran called it, oblivious to the fact that she herself was older than many of those that we visited. Nothing whatever was said about the matter of the utmost importance; and I knew better than to press the point. Like many old people who live alone, Gran talked a great deal whenever she had company and I knew that she would tell me what was troubling her when she was good and ready. After a light evening meal we chatted some more, and watched a television programme that she was particularly anxious to see. Then she said: "I think we'll just go for a little walk, not very far just around the churchyard." Gran lives in a detached house that is set in a comfortable garden, directly opposite the church which is fourteenth century, so a walk round the churchyard was not going to tax either of us very much. The sun had now set and the light was fading but the sky was still perfectly clear. As we came out of Gran's drive and prepared to cross the road, I was struck by the almost complete absence of signs of life. Cars are few and far between in the village nowadays because a new road has taken all the traffic away; and on that particular evening there wasn't even a dog walker about. Gran took us on a small diversion to look at the house of an absent neighbour and make sure that it was in good order and then

34

she led the way through the gate and into the churchyard. I should explain that the churchyard in Gran's village is one of a number in the area which contains both civilian and military graves. The civilian ones cover several centuries, as usual, and come in all shapes and sizes. The military graves all date from 1919 soon after the end of the First World War and almost without exception they mark the final resting place of soldiers from Australia and they are absolutely standard in design. They are about three feet high, arranged in lines, like a platoon on parade. The white headstones carry little more than the number, rank, name and date of death. I have been familiar with these graves since I was a little girl and as I walked through the churchyard with Gran I paid them little attention. I was just listening to her telling me how difficult it was to find anyone who would cut the grass regularly. It did occur to me that Gran was talking even more than usual, and perhaps a little louder than usual, but I made nothing of that: just an old lady's eccentricity. If I noticed anything it was that the soldiers' headstones seemed to glow in the twilight, as if they were softly illumined from within. We went into the churchyard at the west end, walked around the north side of the church, where most of the soldiers are buried, and then began to approach the east end, where there is a huge old yew tree. This yew is older some say, than the church; so old that its trunk has divided into two sections, leaving a gap large enough to walk through. As we approached the east end of the church I began to hear this loud humming noise. At first I thought it might be a swarm of bees or something similar; and I looked around in some alarm. It was a bit too late in the evening for bees I thought and anyway I couldn't see any bees. The loud humming continued and it sounded almost as if it was a human being, making a sort of Mmmmm! sound in appreciation of something, as if someone had tasted something really juicy. I said nothing to Gran and we walked slowly on, with her still prattling away about the churchyard management committee and the curious intractability of its members; which meant that they didn't always agree with her. Then Gran seemed to notice my puzzlement. She stopped and then had a long hard look at me. "What's the matter dear"? She said. "Nothing," I said. "Can you hear that humming noise Gran?" She stopped and listened. "No" she said. "I can't hear anything, not any more. But I used to hear it when I was younger". I looked at her and said, "What is it?" Gran went into her evasive mode. "Oh, nothing to be alarmed about," she said vaguely, as she began to walk on again but very slowly. After a moment I followed her. By now it was almost dark and we were just able to see where we were going. It was at that point that I heard a man's voice, quite distinctly. "It's not fair" said the voice. The man spoke sharply, with a good deal of emphasis and some bitterness. "It's not fair, I say, do you hear me? It's not fair." As you will understand I looked around to see where this voice was coming from. The speaker was obviously some distance away rather than right behind me, but at first I could see no one. I carried on walking, following Gran, who was doddering a bit, looking down to make quite certain where she was putting her feet. I caught up with her as she prepared to walk along the south side of the church, completing our circular tour and heading back towards the churchyard gate. I put my hand on Gran's arm to stop her progress. "Did you hear someone speak?" I asked her. 'No, dear, I didn't hear anything, I was too busy trying to keep on my feet did you hear something"? She asks. "Yes I did I heard someone talking very plainly". I told her. Gran was quite for some time before she said. 'What did they say?' The tone was innocent so innocent that even then I guessed that she knew more than she was admitting. I then told her speaking quite distinctly. "The voice that I heard sounded very much like a young man, he said very clearly, "It's not fair". Gran raised her right arm, "Ah," she said with a slightly guilty tone to her voice. "In that case it was Private Bradshaw. Is he perhaps under the yew tree dear?" I turned to look back at the ancient yew and sure enough, I could now see the dark figure of a man. He was almost hidden under the lower branches. Again I heard him speak, it was almost a shout, with a note of desperation: "It's not fair, not fair at all. I should have had my turn. I never did and that's not right. I won't rest till I do. Do you hear me I won't rest until I do". The voice was now so loud and aggressive that I began to feel a little alarmed. "I think we should go," I said firmly, and took Gran's arm to hurry her along. "Oh you mustn't be frightened of Private Bradshaw,' said Gran. "He sounds a bit fierce but I assure you he is harmless." I looked back at the figure under the tree and was relieved to see that the man had not moved. Now that I looked more closely I could see he was wearing army uniform; his belt buckle sent a brief flash of reflection from the distant street light as did his boots. "Harmless he may be," I said, "but it's very late, and I think we should go home." When we arrived back at the house I locked the front door after us and went round making sure that all the doors and windows were fully secure. Gran meanwhile, made some cocoa. When she handed me my cup I said, "Now then Gran, I think it's about time you told me what that business in the churchyard was all about. Are you going to tell me who Private Bradshaw is, and what he means by hanging around out there?" Gran took refuge once again, in a sort of geriatric fatigue. "Oh not just now dear, I don't think now is the right time. I'll tell you tomorrow. In what is sometimes called the cold light of day." The following morning we took our time about getting up. Then we had a neighbour in for coffee and finally, after the neighbour had departed I told Gran once again that I wanted to hear about Private Bradshaw. "Oh," she said, as if faintly surprised. "I thought you might have forgotten." This was a transparent lie, she thought no such thing. "How could I forget?" I said. "I want to know what on earth this man was doing, lurking about in the graveyard late at night and scaring people half to death by shouting at them. Is he a regular soldier?" I asked Gran. "Oh yes." she replied, "And what does his commanding officer think of him doing that sort of thing?" Gran didn't answer. What I got was a thoughtful question instead: "Tell me, what did the figure under the tree look like to you?" she asks me. "What do you mean, how did he look you saw him, didn't you?" Gran shook her head. "No dear. I can't see him any longer. Or hear him either, though I did once of course, when I was younger." I began to feel worried. "Gran, you're not going blind, are you?" I was quite upset and concerned. "No, no, dear. I'm not blind. Neither am I deaf. Not really." she said. "Well what then?" I think it was at that point that I first began to understand; and despite the warmth of the day, I shivered. "My dear," said Gran, "you've gone quite pale. I'm so sorry I didn't mean to scare you.... I tell you what it might make better sense if we go across the road again. Private Bradshaw won't be there at this time of day that much is quite certain." So that is what we did. Gran led the way and we wandered through the ancient graves until we were among the regular rows of the Australian soldiers. There we found the grave of Private Andrew Bradshaw age seventeen. We stood and looked at the grave together. "He lied about his age" said Gran. "They were farming people his family. Good church-going folk, from New South Wales. This boy was their only son and they needed him on the farm really, but he thought he ought to volunteer for the army and so they all conspired to let him. As soon as he left school he signed the recruitment papers pretending that he was older than he really was. I expect the army knew what he was doing, but they weren't too fussy about details in those days." said Gran. "Did he die in action?" I asked. "Oh no dear nothing like that". None of these men died in action. What happened was, at the end of the war in November 1918, the troops gradually began to drift back to England from France. Of course in an ideal world the troops from overseas Canada, Australia, and so forth they ought to have been sent home immediately. But there were not enough ships available to move them. So lots of the troops were left hanging about in England, with nothing much to do for months on end." I was astonished. "I bet that was popular" I said. "Well exactly, the officers used to take them on endless route marches across the Yorkshire Moors, that sort of thing. I believe some of the Canadian troops actually mutinied in protest against the delays and the futility of wasting time. But that didn't happen here. What did happen of course was influenza." "Influenza" I repeated. "Oh yes, there were epidemics of influenza all over Europe in 1918 and '19, and it wasn't just your usual bad cold and a headache type of flu. This was a killer and it did kill them. Even fit young men killed them by the score as you can see." She looked around at the rows of pale creamy headstones. Suddenly and this was most unlike my grandmother her face seemed to crumple and she grew ten years older, right in front of my eyes. She began to weep. "I met his parents" she said, in between great gulping sobs. "They came over after the second war, because they knew they were going to die soon and they wanted to see his grave. It's my fault you see! That's the worst part. It's all every bit of my fault!' I took Gran home, sat her down and gave her a nice strong cup of tea. It was what she would have done for anyone else in a similar state of distress. When she had regained control of herself I asked her to explain what she had meant about it being all her fault. She sighed deeply and looked down at the damp handkerchief in her hands. "Well it's my fault that Private Bradshaw cannot rest in peace. 'Start at the beginning,' I said firmly. "And go on to the end then stop." For once in her life Gran did as she was told. "You see, at the end of the first war all those Australians died in England, as you well know. They survived all the shooting and killing and then they died of a disease which most of us recover from in a week or two. It is a dreadful irony in itself as here they lie in a foreign graveyard many thousands of miles from their homes and their loved ones. "I don't suppose the dead men were very happy about their situation, but they put up with it, as soldiers do. But then after the Second World War something happened. Something happened to upset them. Well it upset Private Bradshaw, anyway.' I waited but nothing came, so I prodded. "What exactly happened?" Gran took a deep breath before saying; "Well…" there was much hesitation and some embarrassment; a little guilt perhaps. "You see dear at the end of the second war there was a great deal of joy as you can imagine and a good deal of celebration both formal and informal. And I think what happened was, a young soldier and his girlfriend went into the churchyard one night and celebrated in the way that young people do." There was another pause. "You mean they made love?' I asked. "Yes under the Yew tree, quite near to Private Bradshaw's grave.

Too near for his liking." "It can't have been very comfortable for the couple concerned." "Oh, it wasn't too bad" said Gran immediately. "It's all right on a nice warm summer's evening." She gave me a reproving look. "And besides, young people then weren't as free as you are now, you know. They couldn't just say to the family, Excuse us, we're off upstairs for a quickie. They had to be more discreet, take walks in the evening that sort of thing." So at last the rabbit was very definitely out of the hat. I now knew that my grandmother was rather more familiar with the couple in question than had appeared at first sight. "I see" I said totally straight faced. "But just assuming you're right about the couple under the yew tree, why should it be Private Bradshaw who took offence, rather than any of the others?" To Gran it was perfectly obvious. "Oh, because he'd never done it you see, that's why. He'd never made love to a woman himself. He says so doesn't he? "It's not fair," he says. "I should have had my turn, that sort of thing. You've heard him, haven't you?" I had to admit I had. "It was after the Second War and after that bit of, shall we say, informal celebration that people began to hear him for the first time. Well I say people it's only women of course. Women of child bearing age so to speak. Children can't hear him, or see him and the oldies can't either. He's not so bad in the winter he lies quiet for most of the time. But in the summer, in the long hot evenings he is troubled by desire." He is not alone in that I thought, but I said nothing. Gran began to cry again. "The worst thing is that I could have put a stop to it then. And I didn't." she said. "How do you mean, you could have put a stop to it Gran?" "Well I could have gone with him couldn't I? I could have given him what he wanted. I could have given him the experience of having a woman." Her hands twisted together as she sought to express her guilt and shame. "He only wants to do it the once you see. I'm sure of that. It's just that he was so young, and he died so far from home without ever having had a girl of his own. That's what he means when he says it's so unfair and he's right it is horribly terribly unfair." I looked out of the window. Yes, it was still a normal June afternoon, in a perfectly normal English village, with a couple of perfectly normal English women, having a chat about ghosts in the churchyard. "So the figure that I saw and heard last night he was a ghost was he?" Gran wiped her eyes and became very serious. "I prefer to think of him as a presence" she said. "People get frightened and come over all silly when you speak of ghosts. Technically Private Bradshaw is a ghost. A ghost you see is the spirit of a dead person who for some reason remains earthbound. Such a spirit may generate an illusion, that is to say something which is actually unreal, but which looks and sounds convincingly real. That is why you can see him and hear him." "I see" I said. "Well I sort of see. But if he is a ghost then surely he ought to be exorcised." Gran was dismissive, "Oh we've tried that, Last Vicar but one." "And?" I inquired. "The Vicar went into the churchyard late one night with his bell book and candle or whatever and he hadn't got more than three words out when Private Bradshaw punched him full in the face and knocked him flat. The Vicar came out of that churchyard a sight faster than he went in, I can tell you". "I don't know what that ghost wants, Mrs Brownlow," he said to me afterwards, "But one thing he doesn't want is to be exorcised." So that was the end of that. I tried another track. Well why not leave him alone then just let him be. Is he so very troublesome?' "No, not particularly it's only young girls who can hear him clearly, and they tend to keep well away. Or they used to. Modern girls are much bolder I've heard them shout back at him and telling him what he can do with himself, that sort of thing. Well that's not kind and it's not at all helpful." "Time has not mellowed him then." I said. "No they who are gone shall not grow old as we that are left grow old." That thought struck home a bit and I paused. Then I said: 'What does the current Vicar think?' Gran replied, "He raised it at the last churchyard committee meeting and I said that I had an idea for dealing with the matter, so I was appointed. Mrs Jenkins the secretary noted that Mrs Brownlow was appointed as a subcommittee of one to deal with the churchyard ghost. She made a bit of a joke of it. But it's not a joke at all. It's not a bit funny. It's a serious matter, and it has to be dealt with properly. I'm afraid it's a family matter because as I explained, I'm the one who started it all off." There was another pause while I digested what Gran had told me. "Well, if you've been deputed to deal with it, what are you going to do?" I ask. "For a start, I sent for you." Gran said. "Oh" I said. "So it's a plot, is it?" Gran looked just a little bit sheepish. "I'm afraid so. You see, I'm a wicked, scheming old woman." I called a halt at that point as subconsciously I had decided that I didn't want to hear any more, at least for the time being. We went out to lunch at one of the two village pubs before returning home. After Gran then had a nap and a cup of tea, I asked her what she thought I could do to help. "Ah well, you see" she began and I knew at once that she was going to take a roundabout route. "You've heard the noise haven't you; that low, rumbling, murmuring sound." "Yes" I said cautiously. "Well then, that means that Private Bradshaw likes you and you have seen him under the Yew tree and you've heard what he said about it not being fair." "Yes." "Well then…." I genuinely didn't understand even then. I must have looked blank because Gran felt obliged to be more specific. "You're not engaged are you?" she asked. "No" I replied. "Or spoken for in any way?" I told her "No Gran". "Good. I was pretty sure you weren't. It wouldn't do otherwise." "Gran what wouldn't do?" "You see you are exactly the sort of person he needs. Private Bradshaw needs a young, beautiful woman, preferably someone who is not attached to anyone else and who has enough experience to help him. Because he hasn't had any experience." "Do you mean that you think I should go into the churchyard and let Private Bradshaw make love to me?' I said. "Oh yes dear that's the whole point." I must have looked stunned and I was certainly speechless, so Gran continued. "It's not much to ask is it poor Private Bradshaw was robbed and cheated of fifty years of life. He was a perfectly healthy and decent young man, laid low by a terrible virus. And all he asks in return for his sacrifice is a little affection. That's all. He doesn't want a lifetime's devotion or a drawn-out love affair he just wants a few moments of kindness and generosity and sympathy. A little recognition of the sacrifice he made. Now that's not unreasonable, is it? And I'm sure you can put it all right for him if you choose. I mean you have spent two years at University so you are not without experience are you?" At last she stopped for breath, and I almost laughed. But I was forced to admit that she was right about that last bit. "No, Gran" I said solemnly. "I am not without experience." "Oh that's good so you'll do it then?" I sighed deeply. "What precisely do I have to do?" I inquired. "Well, you have to go into the churchyard at midnight tonight." she said. "Has it got to be tonight?" "Oh yes it is midsummer's Eve." There was no arguing with that. "And it's got to be midnight has it?" "Yes that seems the appropriate time to me." "Hmm" I said. "I think I'm going to need a minute or two to think about this."

But of course we both knew that she had me. 'Jolly good" Gran said chirpily. "And by the way whatever happens I don't think we should tell your mother." After tea we went for a walk and watched part of a bowls match. Then we had non-alcoholic drinks in the pub and wandered home at about ten. Gran disappeared into the kitchen. A few minutes later she emerged with a bowl of cereal, made with hot milk. I was mildly astonished, because we didn't normally have any supper. "What's this?" I asked. "Well dear I look at it this way. If I was going to go out into the churchyard at midnight on midsummer's eve to meet Private Bradshaw under the Yew tree I think I would want to get a couple of weetabix inside me first." I was beyond protest by that time. I ate it all up like a good girl. "I think you should wear that blue dress" said Gran. "The one with buttons all down the front nice and easy to get out of and sandals" "And nothing else". I added sarcastically, but Gran thought that I was being vulgar and refused to reply. "I shan't wait up" she said, "any more than I would if you were going to a disco." When I had finished the weetabix she took the bowl from me and tottered off to bed. After about half an hour I changed into the suggested outfit feeling distinctly foolish and self-conscious. Then I waited alone, in silence, until the church clock struck twelve. Perhaps I dozed, I don't know, but the time seemed to pass quite quickly. I turned off all the lights in the house and then went out quietly, through the front door. There I paused for a few moments letting my eyes become used to the gloom. It was fairly dark because there was no moon and there was scarcely a sound to be heard. Just once in the far distance I heard the engine of a car. Then silence again. My feet crunched on the gravel as I went down the short drive, and when I crossed the road I could see no sign of a light in any of the houses. As soon as I reached the gate to the churchyard I heard the hum again that hum of desire as I now realised it was. It was much louder now than the first time, and for a moment I hesitated. As if sensing my uncertainty, the humming stopped and then when I did not run, it began again more intense than ever. Too late to turn back now I thought. I went in through the gate. I saw Private Bradshaw at once. He was waiting for me under the Yew tree. As on the previous night an indirect beam of street light, far away, flickered briefly on his belt and his boots. As I approached the low boughs of the ancient Yew Private Bradshaw came forward to greet me. I could see at once that he was far younger than I had imagined. He was nothing more than a tall lanky boy. Shy and a little reserved. His eyes shone and his belt buckle shone as did his boots which shone like black gold. He had polished them just for me. I led him rather than he me, until we were hidden deep under the Yew tree. When we were both naked and ready I reached out my hand and took hold of his manhood. It seemed quite unusually hot and firm, but then he had been kept waiting for a very long time. After it was all over his hand stroked my face. Then he quietly faded away. Nothing remained of him except his neatly folded uniform and his belt and boots. I could see them clearly defined in the half light of midnight. When I reached out and touched them they were as real as my own hand. But I left them there on the ground. I thought he might need them again. The following morning I was awake at dawn. And when I had gathered my senses I remembered about the uniform. I thought it might somehow alarm people and cause gossip and talk if a soldier's uniform and his boots were to be found under the Yew tree. It might generate enough speculation about the ghost to get into the local press; and then the nationals would pick it up and after that the village would have no peace. I pulled on a few clothes not the blue dress I hurried across the road. I knew exactly where the uniform and the belt and the boots had been left. I went straight to the spot. But of course... there was nothing there...

A

Selection

Of

Children's

Stories

The Wicked Stepmother

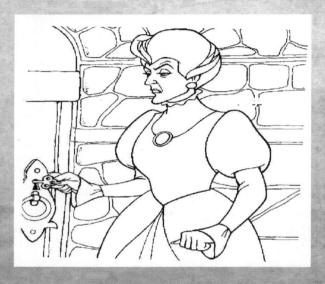

Across the road from Farmer Jessop's field in the country village of Upton, there lived a widow woman and her two daughters. They lived on the edge of a wood where there was a clear bubbling spring of cold water. One of the daughters was very beautiful and a great help about the house, while the other was ugly and idle. The sad thing is that the mother loved only the ugly one, for she was her own child. She cared so little for the other one who was her step- daughter that she made her do all the hard work by earning her living as a Spinner. Day after day the poor girl would sit from morning till night, beside the spring and spin and spin, until her fingers bled. One day, while she was washing the blood from her hands, the spindle from the spinning wheel fell into the water and sank to the bottom. With tears in her eyes, she ran and told her stepmother what she had done. "You must go and get it out." said the angry stepmother.

"You let the spindle fall into the spring. Now you must go and get it out." The poor girl went back to the spring to look for the spindle. She leaned so far over the edge that her hand slipped, and down, down, she sank to the very bottom. The beautiful girl thought that she was having a bad dream. She found that she was in a field where many wild flowers grew. As she walked across the field, she came to a baker's oven full of new bread. The loaves called out to her. "Please pull us out or we shall burn". "Indeed I will" cried the beautiful girl and stepping up; she pulled all the brown loaves out of the oven. As she walked along she came to a tree full of apples. Then as she went past the tree cried out to her, "Shake me, shake me my apples are all ripe and I'm ready to shed them". "Indeed I will" cried the beautiful girl and she shook the tree again and again, until there was not an apple left on its branches. Then she picked up the apples, one by one and piled them in a great heap. When she had picked up all the apples she walked on. At last she came to a small house. In the doorway sat an old woman who had such a large nose that the girl felt afraid of her and turned to run away. Then the old woman shouted, "What do you fear my child, come in and live here with me. If you will do the work about the house, I will be very kind to you. Only take care to make my bed well. You must shake it and Shake it so that the feathers will fly about. Then the children down on the earth will say that snowflakes are falling, for I am Old Mother Frost." The old woman spoke very kindly. "I will gladly work for you," the beautiful girl said. She did her work well, and each day she shook up the bed until the feathers flew about like snowflakes. She was very happy with Old Mother Frost who never spoke an angry word. After the girl had stayed a long time with the kind old woman she began to feel homesick and eventually she said, "Dear Old Mother Frost, you have been very kind to me but I would like to go home to my friends and my family." "I am pleased to hear you say that you wish to go home" said Old Mother Frost. "You have worked for me so well that I will show you the way myself." She took the young girl by the hand and led her to a large gateway. The gate was open, and as she went through it a shower of gold fell over her. It clung to her clothes, so that she was dressed in gold from head to feet. "That is your pay for having worked so hard," said the old woman. "And here is your spindle that fell into the spring". Then the gate closed and the girl found herself once more in the world again. She was not far from her own home, and as she came into the farmyard, a cock on the roof cried loudly: "Cock-a-doodle-doo! Our golden lady has come home too." When the wicked stepmother saw the girl with her golden dress, she was kind to her. Then the girl told her how the gold had fallen on her. The stepmother could hardly wait to have her own child try her luck in the same way. This time she made the idle daughter go to the spring and spin. The lazy girl did not spin fast enough to make her fingers bleed. So she pricked her finger with a thorn until a few drops of blood stained the spindle. She didn't need to wash her hands of the blood so she just let the spindle drop into the water, and sprang in after it herself. The ugly girl found herself in a beautiful field, just as her half-sister had. She walked along the same path until she came to the baker's oven. She heard the loaves cry; "Pull us out, pull us out, or we shall burn!" But the lazy girl said to the brown loaves, "I will not. I do not want to soil my hands in your dirty oven." Then she walked on until she came to the apple tree. "Shake me! Shake me!" the tree cried, "for my apples are quite ripe." "I will not," said the ugly girl, "for some of your apples might fall on my head." As she spoke, she walked lazily on. At last the girl stood before the door of Old Mother Frost's house. She had no fear of Mother Frost's great nose, but walked right up to the old woman and offered to be her servant. For a whole day the girl was very busy, and did everything that she was told to do. The second day she began to be lazy, and on the third day she was even worse. She would not get up in the morning. The bed was never made, or shaken, so the feathers couldn't fly about like snowflakes. At last Old Mother Frost grew tired of her and told her that she must go. This was what the lazy girl wanted, for she felt sure that now she would have to go through the golden gate. Old Mother Frost led her to the great gate, but as she passed under it, a kettle full of black tar was showered over her. "That is what you get for your work," said the old woman, as she shut the gate. The idle girl walked home, covered with tar. When she went into the farmyard the cock on the roof cried out: "Cock-a-doodle-doo! The ugly lady came home, too." The tar stuck so fast to the girl that, as long as she lived, it never came off and from that day on she was never seen in the village again.

The End..........

The Christmas Angel

One Christmas Eve Luke Draper was told to go to bed early and go to sleep as Father Christmas would not come down the chimney, nor would he leave presents if any of the children in the house were still awake. Luke hung up his Red and White topped stocking, (He supports Liverpool), on the mantle-piece of the fire. His mother hung her Green and White stocking to the left of Luke's, and then his father hung his stocking to the right. Luke didn't know why his father had a Red, White, Green and Yellow stocking, he must support some foreign team Luke thought. Luke was asking all sorts of questions about Santa Claus and about his Reindeer so his mother told him about how Father Christmas had a workshop in Lapland were his helpers worked all the year round making toys to give to all the Good children of the world on Christmas Eve. On the way up the stairs to his bedroom Luke was still asking questions; and somehow his mother knew that he would be certain to have a Christmas Eve Dream by the time morning came. Luke was very soon off to sleep as he wanted morning to come as quickly as possible, but he woke up in the middle of the night to see someone sitting on his bed. After rubbing the "Sleep" out of his eyes Luke said. "Hello, who are you?" "I am your Christmas Angel I am here to watch over you for Christmas." The Angel said. "Can you take me to see Santa Claus?" "I can take you to the Little Elves Workshops." said the angel. "Will we be back before Santa brings me my presents?" Luke asked the Angel". Hold on to my wings and we will soon be in Lapland", said the Christmas Angel, and sure enough it was no time before Luke was going over to a small door, to knock on it as the Angel had told him to do when someone answers the door". The Angel said. "Tell them that your Christmas Angel has brought you to see the Elves Workshop". Luke had only a few moments to wait before a Little Elf opened the door and ask him what he was there for. "My Christmas Angel brought me here to see Santa's Workshop and the Little Elves" replied Luke. "I am the foreman of the Elves workshop," said the little Elf. "What would you like to see ..um ah ..um, I don't know your name". "My name is Luke I live in England with my mummy and daddy and my sister Hannah, said Luke. "That's fine Luke if you just follow me I will take you along to the main workshop where you can see all the Father Christmas helpers working very hard to get all the toys ready by morning so that Santa Clause can deliver them to the Good children from all over the world who have sent letters to Father Christmas. "Luke was shown into the workshop where dozens of helpers were hammering and cutting and screwing pieces of wood together to make all different kinds of toys. They were working very hard indeed.

"I have not written to Santa for any toys, does that mean that he will not call at our house then" said Luke to the little Elf - foreman. "Well, as your Christmas Angel brought you here to Lapland, I will take you to see Father Christmas before he loads up his sleigh for him and Rudolf to start their deliveries at Upton were you live." The Little Elf foreman explained to Father Christmas why Luke was at the Workshops and also told him that he had not written to Lapland for any presents. "Well that doesn't matter Luke" said Father Christmas; "I will get my list and you can tell me what it is that you want and one of the Elves will put it on my Sleigh".

"Can I have a present for my mum and dad and my sister Hannah?" Luke asked Father Christmas. "I think we can manage a present for each of them but what do they want?" "I don't know what they want" said Luke. "Can't you tell their Christmas Angels to bring them here?" asks Luke. "I can't do that you see everyone is not as lucky as you Luke, it is only very special people who can see their Christmas Angel" Santa said. "Does that mean that my mum and my dad and Hannah will have nothing in their stockings and no presents to open" asked Luke. "Oh no, we have a little time left before we start our deliveries, so Elf foreman" Santa said to the Elf foreman;

"Get your best little helper to make three special presents for Luke's mother and father and his sister Hannah and put them on my sleigh". "Very well Santa I will do that right away" said the Elf foreman"." That is great Father Christmas" said Luke. "Now Luke you go with the Elf -foreman" said Father Christmas. So Luke and the Elf foreman returned to the Elf workshop. Luke then asked the Elf foreman; "Who built this workshop Elf - foreman". "Come and sit in one of these comfortable chairs and I will tell you the story of the Father Christmas Workshops. When Luke had sat down and made him-self comfortable the little Elf foreman began to tell him the story of the Workshops. The story began a very long time ago. Every Christmas Eve, Santa and Rudolph used to deliver all the toys to the good boys and girls who wrote letters to Father Christmas. The years went by and it was because so many boys and girls wrote letters to Santa saying that they had been really good that the Elves started to run out of room in their workshop. This meant that poor Rudolph who was the only Reindeer at the time was finding it quite hard to fly all the many toys to the many thousands of boys and girls. So Santa got some Magic Dust and turned Rudolph's stable into a bigger workshop for the Elves so that they could carry on making the many more toys that you all receive every year Luke. At first, poor old Rudolph had to stay outside for a few days until Santa realised that he would need a bigger and nicer stable because he was going to get some more special reindeer to help Rudolph. To begin with he got two very clever reindeer and they were called Dancer and Prancer. Everybody thought it was a splendid idea except for some of the younger Elves who thought that the new stable was too far away from their workshop. So Santa suggested that an area be built next to the workshop, then the reindeer could visit whenever they liked. This pleased everybody and they all enjoy the visits of the special new reindeer. But more and more children wrote to Santa every year telling him how good they had been and asking him for more toys. Santa had to get even more Reindeers to help so he got Donner, Blitzen, Comet, Cupid, Dasher and Vixen. After a little while Rudolf, who was the longest serving and the best Reindeer, became the Head of all the Reindeer and he was given a separate stable by himself. Rudolph's stable was built with very special Magic Dust, as he was a very special Reindeer. He had developed a very Red Nose after flying through storms and blizzards in many countries of the world over many years with Father Christmas. After telling Luke the story about the Elves workshop the Elf foreman said to Luke; "Let's go and find Santa". They found Santa in the Very Nasty Weather Hut. He was talking to Johnny the Very Nasty Weather Elf. "How does the weather look Johnny?" asked Santa as Johnny checked the screen. "You know it is only two hours before we start out tonight. I need the final report so that I can plan my journey around the World. We are on a tight schedule this year. There have been so many new good, boys and girls added to my list this year," Santa said as he watched Johnny tinkering with the dials of the Very Nasty Weather Meter. Johnny was twisting and turning the dials, but he was having trouble getting a suitable reading. Never in its 500 years of operation had the Very Nasty Weather Machine failed to provide Santa with the information needed for him to plan a safe route for his Christmas Eve trips around the World. As the little Elf Johnny tried to get a suitable reading Santa Clause could only look on. Suddenly there was a loud explosion and Smoke filled the room. "Goodness me what has happened!" gasped Santa. "We've got a problem," explained Johnny as he examined the damaged machine. "The belt won't turn and I don't know how we'll ever get an accurate reading now" said Johnny. "Just replace the part that is broken and everything should be fine" said Santa. "I am fairly sure we have another cog or whatever it is that is needed" said Santa. "It's not quite as simple as that Santa". Johnny explained as Santa looked puzzled. "The part is deep inside the machine. We don't have the time to take the machine apart to fit a replacement. Besides there is no other way to make the belt turn without the gear that is faulty and remember it has not been changed for almost 100 years, at its last 100 year service" Johnny pointed out. Santa rushed into his Office. He opened his desk drawers one by one as he searched for maps of the routes he had taken back over the years. "It's no good," Santa told the Elves who had gathered around to see what was wrong. "These old maps don't include all the new places for the children we have to visit this year. I have no way of knowing where the storms are tonight. I can't possibly make it around the world without my weather information and there's just no way to turn that belt without a new gear," Santa said, shaking his head. Luke was listening very carefully to Santa's problem as he thought and thought. Then Luke came up with a great idea. "Can I have a word with you Santa" said Luke. "Of course you can Luke, what is it?" Luke then told Santa about his plan to get the belt moving again. "That is a very good idea Luke" said Santa who then told the little Elf foreman to get some of his fittest Little Elves and get them to crawl inside the great machine and find the burned out gear, then to report on the condition of the Belt as this was important if Luke's plan was to work. The result was that the belt seemed in good condition but would not turn because of a broken Cog. This was very good news and the Elves were then instructed to climb up on to the belt. "All you have to do is run on the belt. It will turn and then the machine should work." The Little Elf foreman told his Little Elves. But after several minutes the Little Elves got very tired and there was no room for any more Little Elves inside the great machine. Eventually with one great effort the Very Nasty Weather Machine sputtered just for a few seconds. "We nearly did it then", the Little Elf foreman told the Little Elves. When Johnny the Very Nasty Weather Engineer heard the Nasty weather Machine spluttering he tried to adjust the dials but nothing happened. The Little Elf foreman ordered the other Little Elves to rest for a few minutes then they would make one last effort to start the belt running again. The great Very Nasty Weather Machine gave a few splutters once again, then a kind of groan. The Little Elf foreman was urging his Little Elves to run faster and faster. Suddenly the great Very Nasty Weather Machine burst into life. The screen began to clear.

"Hurry Luke, go and get Santa!" Johnny the Nasty Weather Engineer shouted. "We have a weather report!" he was dancing with joy as Luke and Santa returned panting, from their run across the snow outside the Very Nasty Weather Hut. "How did you do it?" Santa asked Johnny. "It's a mystery to me" replied Johnny, as he handed Santa the weather report. Luke smiled as he moved closer to the Very Nasty Weather Machine. He pushed open the panel at the side of the great machine and out popped all the little helpers who had worked so hard to make sure that all the good children of the world were able to have their presents delivered on Christmas Eve. Soon the loaders were carrying out enough toys to enable Santa Clause to deliver all the requested presents that were asked for in Father Christmas letters. At last it was time for Santa Clause and his faithful Reindeer Rudolf to set off on their long journey around the world to make children in every country happy when they woke up on Christmas Day. But while Luke slept his mother had left a few biscuits for Santa on the window sill. By the early hours of Christmas morning Santa had reached the village of Upton and one of the first houses that he called at was just across the road from where Luke lived. As Rudolf hovered over the house Santa climbed over the side of the Sleigh and lowered him-self by a rope to make sure that everyone in the house was asleep, otherwise he could not leave the presents for the children who lived there. After listening at the chimney for a few moments he was satisfied that everyone in the house was asleep, otherwise he could not leave the presents for the children who lived there. After listening at the chimney for a few moments he was satisfied that everyone was asleep at Luke's house so he went down the Chimney to deliver the special presents for Luke, Hannah and their father and mother.

The End …

The Horse Wore Snow Shoes.

One afternoon during the Christmas school break, the sky became grey and cloudy, Luke Draper had been standing by the window watching for the odd car to pass by, he was bored and the village was very quiet because of the bad weather. Suddenly the air grew thick, and he could scarcely see the houses opposite. Something white and feathery fell slowly down from the sky and rested on the window ledge. Then it disappeared. But more and more of the little flakes came, until there was quite a ridge outside on the window. Luke opened the window gently, fearing that the white flakes might fly away. He was surprised when he touched it to find it was so cold. He took some up in his hand, but in a moment it was only a drop of water. By that time the street and the people's hats and coats who passed by were quite white. Luke was puzzled to find a name for the beautiful white flakes, so he ran to his mother and asked her about it. She told him that it was snow, and because the air was so warm in the City where they used to live, they never got snow there. The next morning Luke saw the other children from the area playing in the snow; but before noon the sun was so bright and warm that the snow had all melted away. A few days later when the second snowstorm came Luke's father got out the beautiful pair of Ice Skates that Santa Clause had brought Luke for Christmas and he had great fun, being pulled up and down the street by his father. Luke soon learned to go out by himself, and made many friends; especially of the girls, as he always let them have a turn to be pulled along by their hands as he moved over the ice and snow on his Skates. But he never forgot that first day when he was surprised by seeing those white beautiful flakes falling. It snowed so hard the next day that Luke had to stay in the house all day. When he went to bed it was still snowing, and every time that he woke up during the night, he could hear the wind sighing and whistling around the old country house where they lived, it also whistled through the branches of the old pine trees in the front garden. "It's not like this in the City" thought Luke. The next morning the sun began to shine. It was a nice day, but cold, and Luke had to again wear thick woollen clothes. "Oh Look Luke, there is a little girl across the road making a snowman in her garden" said his mother. "Mum! Please can I make a snowman after breakfast? "His mum smiled and told him to eat a good breakfast, for making a snowman was hard work. He was soon out in the snow, and what a splendid time he had. Luke's snowman grew very slowly as he had to stop every so often to throw snow-balls at some of his new found friends. When his mother called him in for lunch he wondered where the time had gone since breakfast. But after dinner, Luke was looking out of the window again when he spied two little birds cuddled up on a branch of the pine trees. "Mum! Come and see these poor little birds". "Poor little things," said Luke's mother. "The snow has covered up the places where the birds get their food from" said Luke. "Let's get some food from the kitchen and throw it out to them," said Luke's mother. "They might be able to find it in the snow before more snow comes to cover it up." Said Luke and he was very careful not to throw heavy lumps of bread that would sink in the already heavy falls of snow. Those birds that had perched on posts and fences seemed to be the ones who alerted the other birds that there was some sort of food in the area, as others arrived to take up positions in the pine trees. Soon many birds were chirping and flying about. Luke told his mother that it was the birds saying, "Thank you Luke." Then he told his mother. "It is nice to feed the birds, I am glad that we came to live in the country". But the country also has its share of the Good the Bad and the Ugly for close to where Luke lived was a farmer called Mr Jessop who had a horse that was his pet and his friend. The horse's name was Lord Percy and he carried Mr Jessop everywhere that he wanted to go in the village. The old horse was always happy when his master was in the saddle. But on this particular day the wind was blowing a gale and the snow was very deep. Soon Mr Jessop had to get off the horse and put the saddle away and lead the horse by the rein. They had to stop very often, and shield behind the trees in the fields against the strong winds and the driving snow; while they rested and regained their breath. In places the snow was so deep and soft that he sank to above his knees. It was late in the afternoon that day before Mr Jessop and Lord Percy found shelter in one of the farthest away fields from his farmhouse. They were exhausted, and by the look of the weather it may be a long hard slog to get Lord Percy back to his stable. Suddenly Mr Jessop had an idea that may save him and Lord Percy from staying there any longer than they really needed to. The snow was so deep that Mr Jessop knew that he must go back on snow-shoes, but he was afraid that Lord Percy would have to be left behind until he got some help. He didn't really want to leave Lord Percy by himself in the snow, but he wouldn't be able to help Lord Percy by himself. The old hut where they were taking shelter was one that was used as a "Halfway Workshop" because it was so far away from the farmhouse. It had bits of fencing, rope, odd pieces of wood, a few tools and nails as a means to temporarily patch up and partly mending posts or fences that had blown down in the wind or had been damaged by other animals on the farm. As he was looking around the old hut Mr Jessop had another brainwave. He cut four round pieces of board, twelve inches across, and fastened them on to Lord Percy's legs with rope. Lord Percy seemed to understand what they were for and tried very hard to walk in them. He was very awkward at first and could hardly stand up, but by practising a little he was soon able to manage quite nicely. So Mr Jessop and Lord Percy both returned on snow-shoes to the village street; and how everyone laughed when they saw them. But the people of the village didn't know that Lord Percy never could have made it through the deep snow all that way, if he had not been so very brave and had tried so hard.

The End ....

My Friend the Wind

Daniel and David Thorogood lived in a picturesque village near the Yorkshire Moors. It was a very quiet and pleasant place to live in, but it was very bleak and windy in winter time. One Saturday morning Daniel and his twin brother David were playing in the old car that was behind their father's garage at the side of their house. The cars bodywork was fairly sound but the wheels had been removed some time ago and the car was propped up on some bricks. Nevertheless Daniel and David liked to sit in the driver's seat sometimes and pretend that they were on a racing circuit and hurtling around the track at break neck speeds. The wind got up quite suddenly, as it sometimes did and it got so strong that it blew out the rear windows of the old car. Then it blew over the dustbin and the two children decided to go into the house. Some of the contents of the dustbin were blowing away as Daniel and David tried to pick them up, but every time they tried to catch something the wind whipped it away from them. At this Daniel got very cross. "Stop that!" Daniel said to the wind. But the wind took no notice and only blew their hair across their faces. Daniel's mother had given them a bottle of lemonade to drink so that they wouldn't be running in and out of the house all morning. Daniel had the lemonade bottle, which was now empty, in his hand. He could hardly hold on to the bottle because the wind wanted to blow it away. Daniel was not very happy with the wind, and as she still had the bottle in her hand he suddenly made a swipe with it, put the cork on; and screwed it tight. He pushed the hair

66

back out of his eyes and said, "Now I've got you." "What have you got?" asked David. "I've caught the wind," said Daniel as she pointed to the bottle and smiled. "You haven't" said David as he was one of those boys who didn't believe anything that he couldn't see, like the wind for instance. "I have got it" said Daniel as she held the bottle up to his ear. "Listen" she said to David. "It's talking to me." "No it isn't" said David. But at the same time he thought that he had better just have a listen; and sure enough, David heard it as well. "Let me out" said the wind in a very tiny voice that was very faint. "Let me out and I won't tease you anymore." The wind said. But Daniel thought about all the times that the wind had been loud and noisy and rough and had kept him awake at nights. On the other hand David couldn't bear to think of the wind shut up inside the bottle, so he took the bottle from Daniel unscrewed the cork and shook the bottle out. As it escaped the wind smelt of lemonade from having been shut up in the bottle during the morning. "Thank you David" the wind whispered as it blew a little circle of twigs around his feet. "If ever you want or need me just whistle." the wind said. Then the wind died away and the air was still and heavy. Daniel tried to whistle but she could only blow. David of course knew how to whistle as he had been taught by his father how to whistle. Daniel didn't trust the wind. Both of the children went back into the house and Daniel told his mother about the dustbin. Even though Daniel **couldn't** whistle and David **wouldn't** whistle, the wind came to play with them from time to time. It was never rough or loud and the games were very exciting that they played with the wind. Then summer came and the days grew longer and hotter and the wind didn't come any more. Daniel tried to whistle, but she could only **blow**. "The wind's gone on holiday" he said sadly. "Let it stay on holiday" said David and he **wouldn't** whistle. But one day when Daniel and David were playing in the garden their cousin Joshua, who had come to visit, came out of the house to tell them. "The man from the Bank is coming to take the house away." "Why?" Daniel asked. "Why is the Bank Man going to take our house away?" "Your Daddy owes him some money and he can't pay it back yet. So he is taking the house instead." said Joshua. "He can't" said Daniel. "We need it to live in." said David, "We need help", Daniel said trying to whistle but he could only **blow**. "You whistle for the wind David" said Daniel. "Please whistle for the wind." But David **wouldn't** whistle. Then when morning came, there was the Bank Man's car coming along the road and up the hill, behind it was a Police car. The entire village came out to watch. The Bank Man's car stopped at Daniel's front door and the Bank Man got out. The Police car stopped and one of the Policemen got out and straightened his cap on his head. They started to walk along the short path towards the house. Daniel tried to whistle for the wind but he could only **blow**. "Whistle David, whistle for the wind" shouted Daniel through his tears. David thought about not having anywhere to live and nowhere to sleep. After a few minutes David **whistled**. At first very low but then he whistled loud and long. They waited for the wind to answer but everything was quiet except for the plodding of the policeman's feet on the pathway. Suddenly Daniel heard the wind as it came up the hill, then it reached the trees in the front garden. The wind was all around them, lifting their hair and blowing twigs and leaves along the street. "Stop them" David shouted to the wind. "Stop the Bank Man and the Police from taking our house." "Watch me David" said the wind. It came up the garden path and turned towards the Bank Man and the Policeman. First it blew the hat off the

Bank Man and the cap off the Policeman. Then it blew the wig off the Bank Man's head. Then it blew the Bank Man into the Policeman, so that they both fell on the ground in a heap. Then it blew both of them back up the garden path and out through the front gate and into the street. The Bank Man and the Policeman looked angry when they got to their feet as their clothes were covered with dirt and dust. They started to walk up the street but the wind blew them back down the hill. The Policeman went back to the Police car and the Bank Man tried to walk forward again. This time the wind blew him into a field through all the bushes, and blew him into the stream at the bottom. The Bank man crawled out of the stream covered with weeds and mud and he ran back to the road. The Policeman picked him up in his car and the wind was heard to say; "Be Gone from this village" as it blew the Police car outside the village boundaries. The Man from the Bank never came back again and David was delighted when he told Daniel; "There is no better friend than the wind".

The End ....

The Newcastle to London Express

Luke and his sister Hannah lived in the East of England. Twice yearly the families all spent their Summer Holidays and their Christmas breaks at their Grandfather Estate that overlooked a beautiful valley with a long winding Canal flowing away to the left of the house. The children loved to hide in and climb the dense trees that surrounded the house. On the other side of the Canal there was a railway line, along which the main London to Newcastle train travelled, as did other trains to various other locations. The trees, the bridges, the trains, the boats, the valley and the Canal were all to play their part in Luke and Hannah's adventurous dreams which only seemed to occur after they had been hurt, falling from a tree, or taking a tumble from running too fast into the valley, which they named The Valley of Dreams. Their first Dream adventure started when Luke and Hannah were watching one of the bridges that spanned the railway and the Canal, and which had a tow path along its bank. It was common knowledge that the train drivers blew their whistles and the navigators of the Canal boats, tooted their horns as they approached the bridges so that the local children could wave to the train or boat as they passed over or under the bridges. Luke and Hannah's Grandparents owned all the ground covering the estate and the valley, as far as the Canal, which was part of the Waterway Network called the Big Union Canal. It stretched for more than 130 miles from Birmingham to London, with waterway arms to Brookville, Windover, Glenbury and Eastecton. Sometimes their Grandfather would take the children fishing on his boat that could sleep about eight people. The boat was quite close to the house and the moorings that led into the Canal. One holiday day out was supposed to be a picnic in the valley alongside the Canal. It was normally Luke and Hannah's job to find a spot for the picnic. On this occasion it was very hot and the children had to find somewhere to shelter from the sun. They found a lovely spot with plenty of shade among the trees. They had just finished setting up the tables and chairs when they heard the whistle from one of the trains. "Luke, let's go to the bridge and wave to the train" said Hannah. "Race you there" said Luke and they both ran off as fast as their young legs could take them in the direction of the bridge that the train was approaching. Hannah was running so fast that she tripped on a dip in the grass and fell over. Luke was well ahead of her but when he looked back he could see her lying very still on the ground. Luke at once ran back towards Hannah and as he ran he was calling out to her, "Come on Hannah, quickly or you will miss the train". But there was no answer from Hannah. "Oh dear" cried Luke as he could see that Hannah was not moving and her eyes were shut as she lay on the grass. Luke tried very hard to wake her but she just lay there very still. Luke was muttering to himself, "I must go and tell daddy" as he ran towards the spot where they had left the others. As he ran he was calling out " Daddy Daddy come quickly ". All the time he could hear the sound of the great train behind him.

Clickity Click , Clickity Click , Clickity Click .

When Hannah opened her eyes the sun was so bright that she could hardly focus properly. As she looked ahead all she could make out was a hazy outline of a train. Through the mist and steam from the train Hannah suddenly realized that the train had stopped. "I've never seen a train stop here before" she thought. She imagined that she could also see someone waving to her from the engine of the train. As she drew nearer she could make out the figure of the train driver in his train uniform. "Hello little lady" called the driver across the Canal, "What is your name"? "I am Hannah and I live in the large house across the valley" she said. The Engine Driver stepped down on to the track so that he was nearer to Hannah and he did not need to shout across the Canal to her. "Would you like to come on to the footplate of the engine"? The driver asked. "Can my brother come too"? Hannah inquired. The driver said that he could not see her brother. "That's okay" said Hannah. "I shall go and find him". She then ran off and very soon returned with Luke by her side. "This is my brother Luke" Hannah said to the driver. "We would both like to see the engine please". Hannah and Luke then walked the short distance to the bridge, crossed over to the other side and went to the engine where the driver helped them on to the footplate. "Now then young Hannah and Luke" said the driver, "What do you think of the engine then"? "It's much bigger than I thought it would be" said Luke. "And much cleaner too" said Hannah. "Yes, you see the brass work inside and outside must be cleaned each night by the night shift in the engine shed, they work from 8pm until 4am everyday" said the driver. Hannah then ask "Why is the train stopped here"? "There seems to be some sort of a problem further up the track" the driver told her. He was pointing down the track as he further explained that a signal had been turned ON which meant that he had to stop and wait until it was turned OFF before he could continue his journey. "Can I reverse the train a little way back up the line"? Ask Hannah. "Oh goodness me, no" said the driver, "But, when the signal changes to OFF you can drive us into London". He told Hannah. "Oh thank you" cried Hannah and then she said to her brother. "Luke did you hear that I am driving the train to London" She could hardly believe that she was to drive the train and she was very excited. But she noticed that Luke was very quiet so she said to him, "Are you frightened of me driving the train Luke". Luke said "Not really, I was just wondering what I could do, that's all". At this point the driver turned to Luke and said. "Don't worry Luke I have a very important job for you to do. You will be responsible for making sure that there is enough head of steam throughout the rest of the journey". He paused for a few seconds, then he said; "You see Luke if you don't maintain the correct steam pressure the train will slow down, we will not get to our destination on time and the passengers will be late for their work in London". Luke was very pleased that he had an important job to do and he said, "I'm glad that I came on the train." Hannah was looking at the controls and she suddenly said to the driver. "Where is the fireman for the train then" The driver said that the fireman had taken ill that morning and there was no one else available so he had to take the train out on his own and do both the jobs, otherwise the train would have to be cancelled and all the passengers would not have been able to get to work. While they were waiting for the signal to change the driver was showing Hannah where to sit. She had to sit on a little box on top of the seat by the driver's window to enable her to reach the starting lever and the trains whistle control. Luke also had a try at opening the fire box door and feeding a few shovels-full of coal on to the fire. The train driver was happy that both Hannah and Luke knew what to do so it was now just a matter of waiting for the signal to change. Luke noticed that it had started to rain and that there was a bit of a breeze blowing. Hannah ask the driver, "How do you know that you have to stop and how does the signal work"? "Well" explained the driver, "Stop signals are normally an arm with a red face and a white stripe on the front; and from the opposite direction it is a white face with a black stripe". The driver continued to explain that when a signal arm is horizontal it is said to be on and of course when it is either raised or lowered it is said to be OFF. He said that their meanings were very simple, when the signal is ON the train must stop and when it is OFF the section is clear all the way to the next signal stop. "So you see Hannah a driver must never pass a stop signal that is ON, unless authorized to do so by the Signalman". "What does a Signalman do" ask Luke. The driver told both of them that the Signalman works in a signal box which is near to a Railway Station. His job is to put the train on to the proper rails for the route into the station,; and he does this by pulling a lever in the Signal box which puts the train on the correct rail for the correct platform. "The first indication the signalman will have that a train is approaching is when it first arrives on his track circuit indicator in the signal box". The driver continued to tell them that the signalman monitors the progress of the train on the circuit track; and by pulling appropriate levers he can direct the train to an empty platform. He will advise the station staff by ringing the platform bell; once for platform one, or twice for platform two", the driver told Hannah. By this time some of the passengers had become a little restless and they got down from the train on to the track in order to find out what was happening. Some of them thought that there had been an accident. The driver told Luke and Hannah that he would have to get the guard to instruct the passengers to return to their seats before the signal changed, he therefore left the engine and went to the guards van of the train. He was back very quickly and he told Hannah to keep her eyes on the signal. Suddenly Hannah got very excited, "The signal has changed, it's changed, can we go now can we go". The driver calmly said "Ok Hannah just pull the lever nice and steady, don't jerk it, just a steady pull". As she pulled down on the lever the train started to move, very slowly at first, Chug, Chug, but picking up speed every second until it was travelling very fast into the lovely countryside. Luke was keeping his eyes on the temperature gauge and occasionally opening the fire door to shovel more coal into the fire box. Hannah and Luke were able to admire the scenery, but as they approached a little town the rain was coming down quite heavily. Hannah could see that the signal was OFF. "That's okay" she thought, "We just carry on through this station until we come to the next stop signal" .As the train sped through the station the weather was getting worse. A strong wind had got up and the rain was very heavy. "Hey Luke" said Hannah, "If the rain stays as heavy as this you won't have to take on any water at the tank". "Yea" said Luke, "But it is the strong wind that I am worried about, it could blow me off the Tender when I climb up there". Hannah reached up and pulled the lever that blew the train whistle when she saw that they were coming up to a Bridge. They could not see any people or children to wave to. Luke said that this was probably because of the bad weather, but just a short way past the bridge he did notice that there was another bridge, over a roadway, where some trees looked as though they had been blown down with the strong winds, or they may have been struck by lightning in a recent storm. Hannah realized that when travelling at speed on a train the weather conditions can change very quickly and the trees were quite close to the rail track and could be very dangerous. She decided to take no chances so she slowed the train down. The driver was not very happy, "We will be late if we slow down" he said. Hannah was looking out at the misty haze and she said to the driver, "Look at all the water in the fields and the weather is getting worse" They then came to a bend and only a short distance away from a large tree that had fallen across the track. Hannah at once applied the brakes and the train slid along the track and came to a standstill only a few feet from the tree. The screeching of the wheels on the track and the sudden stop caused some of the passengers to lean out of the windows to see what had happened. Some of them were again getting down on to the track. One person seemed very annoyed. He told the driver that he was going to make a complaint when he gets to the station. The driver explained to the gentleman that if it had not been for the quick thinking and the reactions of Hannah, the train would most certainly have been derailed. He then added, "And now sir I must find a telephone quickly". "You may use my mobile phone it's the least I can do under the circumstances" the gentleman said. The driver thanked the gentleman and contacted the signalman at the next station. He then returned the mobile phone to the gentleman and told him that the appropriate departments would be informed and that all that can be done now is to make sure that everyone returns to the train to check that no one is hurt or missing, as buses would probably be sent to take the passengers to their final destinations. When all the passengers returned to their seats it emerged that the passenger who was complaining was a Newspaper Editor. He was very interested in the story of how Hannah had prevented what may well have been a disaster. It was to be some time before the track could be cleared. The driver always brought a packed lunch with him; as sometimes he had to fit in where and when he was needed and therefore couldn't be sure if he would be near a Café or a Canteen. On this particular day he shared his flask of tea and roast pork sandwiches with his new found friends Hannah and Luke. They were both very pleased as they never thought that their picnic was going to be on the footplate of the London to Newcastle Express. It was a magnificent sight when the train eventually approached under a large bridge, where most of the townspeople had gathered. Luke's Steam could be seen for miles around. Luke had worked very hard to get the train to its final destination. But the Day belonged to his sister Hannah. She had saved the crew and all the passengers from almost certain disaster. The people, the pressmen and all the photographers were there only to see Hannah. The Newspaper Editor had alerted his office in London and the word soon got around about the train incident. The passengers had all been transferred to buses and were in many cases at their workplaces by now. As the train approached the platform Hannah and Luke could see that it was lined with people. At first they thought that it was a very busy station but the driver said that the Police had requested that the train be diverted to a less busy platform for the benefit of the pressmen and photographers. When the train stopped Hannah was the first to get on to the platform. Just as she was saying goodbye to the driver a great cheer went up and the very large crowd that had assembled began to cheer and shout.

Everyone wanted to get a photograph of the little girl who saved the train from disaster. "We want Hannah……Hannah….Hannah", they were shouting. Then the chanting got louder and louder. "HANNAH, are you all right"

Hannah opened her eyes to see her mother bending down to pick her up in her arms. All Hannah could say was; "Mummy, Luke is still on the train". This was the first time that any of the children had fallen or been hurt and had an adventure dream. But there were more dreams and adventures to come during future holidays.

The End..............

The Lost Reindeer

It was the night of the year when few children can sleep. The night when everyone hopes that snow will fall and they will wake up to a garden of glistening diamonds that were grown by the morning sun. It was Christmas Eve. Many had hoped for snow to fall and it did, as it slowly covered the houses and streets in a thick white blanket. The moon shone its silver light down on the white world, but for one person, there was nobody to view the kind of beauty that things such as love and dreams are made of. The only one there to see the spectacle was a small boy of five years of age. Luke Draper had just moved to a new house in the country. It was in the month of October and five years after Luke was born. His father and mother had written to Father Christmas at Lapland to ask for the little Elves to make a pair of Skates as a Christmas present for Luke. They thought that as the snow lies on the roads and the fields much longer in the country, it would be better and much easier for Luke to ride around on Skates rather than on a bicycle in the snow and icy roads. So Luke was hoping that it would snow on Christmas Eve then he could try out his new Skates on Christmas morning. The house where they lived was behind the old church in the village of Upton, and they could hear the church choir rehearsing their Carols for the Christmas Service. The house was heated by an open coal fireplace; and one day they had a fire of logs on the hearth. Luke enjoyed it very much, and thought that the bright log fire was very cosy. He had never seen an open fire before, and he was pleased that they also had a chimney for Santa Claus to come down to deliver his Skates. A few days before Christmas Eve Luke went to play with some of his new friends in a field near his home. They were playing Football and Luke had run to collect the ball from behind a large old Oak Tree. As he bent down to collect the ball he heard a noise, it was a rustling kind of noise on the other side of the tree. He had a quick peek to see what was causing the noise and he couldn't believe his eyes. There in the field was a Reindeer with bright red bells all around its harness.

"Where did that come from" Luke thought as he kicked the ball back to the playing pitch and went to have a look at the Reindeer. "He must have come from one of the Farmer's stables" Luke said out loud. "I must take him back to his stable, as his owner will be looking for him "."No, no you mustn't", a gentle voice said. Luke turned round and looked to see who had spoken, but there was no one there except the little Reindeer. "Who said that?" Luke shouted loudly. "It's me", said the little Reindeer very quietly. "You can talk?" spluttered Luke. "Yes, I can" said the Reindeer. "There are no schools for talking Reindeer around here" said Luke. "I will explain everything later" said the Reindeer. "But first, I must tell you how I got here. You see not all countries in the world celebrates Christmas on the same day and I was the Reindeer chosen by Santa Claus to deliver presents to the children from Ireland, who had written to him for Christmas presents. "The Reindeer went on to explain that Father Christmas had got letters from Ireland asking for presents for Little Christmas, which in Ireland is celebrated on the sixth of December every year. It is called Little Christmas because it was, until the adoption of the Gregorian calendar, the day on which Christmas Day was originally celebrated. It is the traditional end of the Christmas season and the last day of the Christmas school holidays. It is also known in Ireland as the Woman's Christmas because of the tradition of Irish men taking on all the household duties on that day and giving their wives the day off. "Well Luke", the Reindeer continued. "As I was coming over the coast of Spain I must have taken a wrong turning and I had to land here. The sky was very thick with fog in the English Channel and it was not possible to stick to any of our usually known landmarks". "Who owns you?" Luke asked. "Santa Clause" the Reindeer replied. "Santa doesn't live around here" Luke said. "You come with me and all will be revealed" said the Reindeer. "Do you want me to help you to get back to Santa Clause?" asked Luke. "Yes Please". Said the Reindeer and he and Luke set off on a long journey. Luke had climbed on to the Reindeer's back and asked him what his name was. "My name is Dancer," the Reindeer said. Luke soon got comfortable on Dancer's back and they set off over the mountains with the breeze blowing in their faces, it was great. Luke had never had so much fun. After a while they stopped for a rest. Dancer ate some grass nearby while Luke just sat there resting and getting his breath back. It took quite a while as Dancer must have been very hungry, and Luke was also getting thirsty. He heard water flowing nearby and realised that there was a stream, where he managed to get a drink before they were off again over the forests and over the hills. The last time Luke looked down he saw little mountains of white ground here and there. But when he looked down again it was everywhere, not just on top of mountains but covering them all over. Luke had never seen White ground before. Then they suddenly came to a stop. Luke looked up and there in front of him was a very large building full of sweets and toys. "This is the Elves Workshop" the Reindeer told Luke. Then Luke heard the Reindeer call out, "Santa, Elves, I'm back home, it's me Dancer and I've got a friend with me." At first there was no reply and Luke thought that there was no one else there. Suddenly he heard the sound of a train, and soon out of the workshop emerged a beautiful Red train with a driver dressed in a red cloak and with him were several little Elves. Santa was driving the train and there were wagon loads of all sorts of toys that the Elves had made in the Workshop for all the good children who had written to Father Christmas for presents. "Oh, there you are Dancer" said Santa when he saw Dancer and Luke by the entrance to the Elves Workshop. "And who have you brought with you is this another little helper"? "No Santa" said Dancer. "This is Luke Draper he kindly helped me after I had got lost on my way from Ireland, after delivering the toys to the children for Little Christmas." "Thank you Luke, for bringing Dancer home we were all very worried when he got lost," and Luke could see that Santa did look worried. "For helping Dancer I shall give you a very special present," Santa whispered to Luke. Then he clicked his fingers and a little Elf came with a large green box and a red ribbon tied around it. Santa gave the present to Luke, but before he could say thank you to Santa, or anything else, Luke was back in the field next to the Oak tree where he had found Dancer the Reindeer. Luke went straight home as fast as he could with his present, and told his mother all about Santa and Dancer the Reindeer. "Mummy, Will you open the present that Santa gave to me for helping Dancer" Luke asked his mother. "Give it here Luke and let's see what Santa has given you from the Little Elves Workshop". Luke could hardly wait for his mother to unwrap the present. At last all the paper wrapping was off to reveal a box with a red lid. "I wonder what is in the box" thought Luke. "It's not long enough to be a pair of Skates and it is too long to be a football, but it might even be a racing car". Soon the long wait was over as Luke's mum opened the final piece of paper from the present. "Oh look Luke" said his mother. "How did Father Christmas know that you wanted a computer of your very own"? "We had better switch it on Luke to make sure that it is working properly" said Luke's father, who then plugged it into the wall socket. Everyone was huddled around the computer waiting, as it seemed to take ages to warm up. "Won't be long now" said Luke's father. "Just one mouse click, Wow, can you see that Luke, look at the screen" he said. Both Luke and his mother turned to look and there on the screen was a message from Father Christmas which read;

The End…………..

Something very special was happening for Christmas, as the local Member of Parliament in the village of Upton had decided to hold a Christmas Ball for all the children of the village, the poor ones as well as the rich ones. The preparations for this ball had been going on for several weeks. Posters and leaflets were given out and it was advertised in all the local newspapers with headlines like;

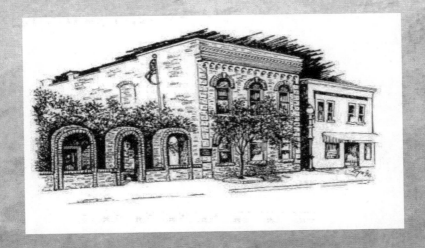

THE M.P.'s MASQERADE BALL

The MP had promised to meet the expenses for all the poor children whose parents were unable to do so, and the bills for their costumes were to be sent to him. He was looked upon by the villagers as "The Village Squire" There was great excitement among the regular people of the village, as they all wanted to compete with each other to see which child was the most popular, on this very special Christmas occasion in their village. The posters and the notices had not been out more than a week before a newcomer came to the village. He set up his shop on the corner of the main street. He hung up his beautiful costumes in the window of his shop so that everyone could see them when they wanted to. He was a little fellow, not much bigger than a boy of ten or eleven years old. His cheeks were as red as roses, and he had on a long Red coat and a curling wig and beard that were as white as snow. He sat on a high stool behind his counter and served his customers by himself, he had no assistants or anyone else to help him. It didn't take the children long to discover what beautiful costumes he had; and how much better he was than the other shopkeepers in the village. So they all flocked to his shop. Everyone from the Squire's daughter, to the poor rag and bone man's children. The idea was that the children were to select their own costumes and the Squire had made it clear that it was to be a children's ball in every sense of the word. Some children had decided to be fairies, or shepherdesses and some even chose to be princesses; and this new Shopkeeper had every beautiful charming costume to suit them all. It was strange that the children of the rich, who had everything that they wanted, choose the parts of beggars or peasants. On the other hand, the poor children jumped at the chance of being princesses or fairies even though it was only for a few hours in their mostly miserable young lives. One peasant's son chose to be The Chief of Police, and his costume fitted him perfectly. At exactly twelve noon on the Saturday before Christmas Day, the children flocked to the Squire's mansion house on the hill at the edge of the village. They all looked the part that they were playing. Those who were dressed as little fairies looked like fairies and danced like fairies. It was hard to imagine that they were in fact Hannah Stokes the washerwoman's little girl, and Polly Saunders, the charwoman's little girl. The Squire's youngest daughter, who had chosen the character of a Shepherdess, looked so like a true one that you could hardly imagine she was anything else. She was in fact a slender, little lady, but tall for her age. She now looked very short and brown, just as if she had been tending sheep in all kinds of weather. It was the same with all the others. The Red Riding-hoods, the Princesses, the Bo-Peeps, and with every one of the characters who came to the Squire's ball. It was all great fun, as the fiddlers fiddled and fiddled, and the children danced and danced on the beautiful waxed floors. The Squire, with his family and a few grand guests, sat on a platform at one end of the dance floor, and watched the children enjoying themselves. Supper was served and what a supper. The piles of pink and white ices, the cakes made with iced castles, and the gold and red jellies. Under each child's seat there was a pretty present and every one had a little basket of sweets and a cake to take home. At nine pm, the fiddlers put away their fiddles and the children filed out of the Squire's house and went down the hill to their homes. Fairies and Shepherdesses Pages and Princesses were all jabbering gleefully about the splendid time that they had. But it was all short lived; for when the proud parents tried to take off their children's costumes in order to prepare them for bed, not a single costume would come off. The buttons buttoned again as fast as they were unbuttoned; when a string was untied it tied itself up again into a knot. The parents became frightened, but the children were so tired out that they were allowed to go to bed in their fancy costumes, as the parents thought that they would come off much easier by the time morning came. BUT....at exactly midnight on that Children's Christmas Ball night, all the children woke up. A great wave of alarm spread over the village as the costumes still wouldn't come off. But that was not the worst of it. Every one of the children seemed to have become the character which he or she had assumed. The Squire's daughter said that she was going to tend her sheep out in the fields, and the peasant boy told his mother that as the Chief of Police, he would investigate what was happening. It was all so mysterious, and the news spread very quickly beyond the village. Very soon a great crowd had gathered around the new shopkeeper's shop at the end of the main street. Everyone thought that he must be the one responsible for all that had happened. The shop door was locked, but very soon the men of the village battered it down. When they rushed in, the Shopkeeper was not there; he had disappeared and all his costumes were gone. The Squire then called a meeting of all the residents, and they assembled in the Village Hall. As the Chief of Police, the peasant boy was the only child at the meeting which the Squire opened by telling them what had happened so far. One of the villagers was a Mr Roberts who was a widower and lived on his remote farm on the edge of the village. "What did this Shopkeeper look like?" Mr Roberts asked. The peasant boy, as the Police spokesman, told Mr Roberts about the little red coated shopkeeper with the red face, white wig and beard. He also said that a great many detectives were out looking for the shopkeeper. "I know where he is" said Mr Roberts. "He is up in one of my Cherry-trees. He's been living there ever since the Cherries were ripe, but he won't come down." In a very short time, half of the people of the village were on the road to Mr Robert's farm. He had a beautiful orchard of cherry-trees all laden with fruit. Sure enough, in one of the tallest of the trees, way up amongst the branches, sat the Shopkeeper in his Red velvet clothes and his long black boots. "Good-morning" he shouted as he saw the people below.. The Squire shook his gold-headed walking stick at him, and the people danced around the tree in a rage. Then they tried to climb the tree, but they soon found that it was impossible. As fast as they put a hand or foot to the tree, back it flew with a jerk exactly as if the tree had pushed it. They tried a ladder, but the ladder fell back the moment it touched the tree, and lay sprawling on the ground. They brought axes and thought they could chop the tree down, shopkeeper and all.. But the wood of the tree resisted the axes as though it was made of Steele. During all this time the shopkeeper sat up in the tree eating cherries and throwing the stones down to the ground. Finally he stood up on a strong branch and looking down, he said; "It's no use trying to solve your problem in this manner, we must talk about the situation and I'm willing to come to terms with you, and to make everything right on two conditions." The people on the ground were very quiet then, and the Squire stepped forward as the village spokesperson. "Name your two conditions," the Squire shouted up to the Shopkeeper. "But remember that you alone Mr Shopkeeper, are the cause of all this trouble". "Well" said the shopkeeper, reaching out for another handful of cherries, "This Christmas Ball of yours Squire was a great idea, but you wouldn't do it every year, and your successors in the future might not do it at all. I want those poor children to have a good Christmas

EVERY year. My first condition is that every poor child in the village hangs their stockings up for gifts in the Village Hall on every Christmas Eve, and gets them filled too.. I want this in writing and filed in the Council archives." said the shopkeeper. "We agree to the first condition!" cried all of the people without waiting for the Squire to answer the Shopkeeper's condition. "The second condition is that the Squire's elder daughter marries this good Cherry-man's son as he has been very kind to me, letting me live in his cherry-tree and eat his cherries, so I want to reward him." "We consent," shouted all the people; all that is, except the Squire. "I will not consent to the second condition," The Squire shouted up to the shopkeeper angrily. "Very well then" said the shopkeeper; "Your daughter can tend sheep for the rest of her life, that's all." The Squire was very upset; but the thought of his younger daughter being a shepherdess for the rest of her life was too much for him and he eventually agreed. "Now go home and take the costumes off your children," said the Shopkeeper and leave me in peace to eat my cherries." The people all went back to the village, and found, to their great delight that the costumes would now come off. The buttons stayed unbuttoned, and the strings stayed untied. The children were dressed in their own proper clothes and were now their own proper selves once more. The shepherdesses and the chimney-sweeps came home; the princesses and the fairies put on their own suitable dresses and went about their usual business. There was great joy in every home in the village. The Squire's youngest daughter thought she had never been so happy, now that she was no longer tending sheep, but her own dainty ladylike self. The village council passed a resolution to provide every poor child in the village with a stocking full of gifts on every Christmas Eve, which was filed and put in the village archives. The Squire's other daughter was married to the Cherry man's son and all the children of the village came to the wedding. They threw flowers in her path till her feet were hidden in them. But the shopkeeper had disappeared from the Cherry-tree on the night before the wedding. He had left at the foot of the tree some beautiful wedding presents for the happy couple. A silver tray with cherries engraved on it, a set of china with cherries on it; and two white satin robes, His and Hers, with cherries down the front of them. From that very day the Squire's daughter and her husband and everyone in the Village lived happily ever after.

The End...........

A Safari Dream Adventure

Luke   &   Hannah

Hannah liked her hamster and her Grandmother Bernie's cat and lots of other animals. She was convinced that she could talk to some of the animals as her next door neighbours' dog barked every time she spoke to it. Her grandmother promised Hannah that if she was a good girl, she would take her to the Safari Park as a special treat on her birthday which was on the 22nd February. "Can my brother Luke come too" Hannah asked her grandmother. "Only if you are a good girl and there is to be no fighting between you two", her grandmother told her. So on the night before her birthday Hannah went off to bed saying; "I hope it doesn't rain or anything tomorrow as I want to talk to the animals". Much later that evening Hannah's mother looked into her bedroom. Hannah was twisting and turning and mumbling about Tigers…Bears….lions. This was a sign thought her mother, that Hannah was having a Dream Adventure, being very excited about going to see all the animals in the Safari Park which was just outside the Town; and as always mothers are usually right about these things. Hannah, Luke and their grandmother got the number 4 bus that stopped outside the gates to the Safari Park. Hannah and Luke were ahead of Grandmother Bernie as usual as Hannah always liked to be the first to get to wherever they were going to. "Here it is" said Hannah as they came near to a large sign which was above the entrance to the Animal Safari Park.

"I want to see the large animals first" said Hannah as they came through the main gate, she could see the long neck and the head of a Giraffe.

"Let's go and see the Giraffe" she said as they walked along a pathway to where the Giraffe was living. Luke didn't know which animals to look at first and as he looked to see where Hannah was heading for, he stopped in his tracks.

He could not believe his eyes as he saw two huge African Elephants having a walk with their baby Elephant, just like as though they were having a stroll in a park.

The next animal that they came to was a large Gorilla. As Hannah went nearer to have a better view the Gorilla stood up and started to beat his chest.

Both Hannah and Luke thought that it was going to escape and jump over the fence of the compound where he was living, so they moved quickly away along the concrete pathway.

"He's got the same name as me Luke the Lion" shouted Luke as he spied a young lion cub.

His name was very clearly painted on the back of his cage. "Maybe he can talk to me" said Hannah as she moved closer to the cage and said; "Hello Luke that's the same name as my brother Luke here. I am Five"? But to her disappointment the Lion didn't make any reply he just stared out of his cage.

"Let's try over there" said Luke pointing to an enclosure just across the pathway. "I can see some baby Tigers." said Hannah.

As they moved towards the baby Tigers Hannah was sure that these two little fellows were pleased to see her. "Hello little Tigers" said Hannah. "What are your names this is my brother Luke would you like to talk to us, the little tigers stood there looking lovely but saying nothing.

Further along the pathway which went all the way round the Park they saw one of the Animal Keepers walking along with an Elephant. "Can I speak to your Elephant" Hannah said to the Zoo Keeper. "Of course you can, but you must not give her any food as she has her own special food here at the Safari Park". "What is the Elephant's name asks Hannah." She is called Hannah" the Zoo Keeper replied. "Oh that is my name" Hannah said. Then she asked the Elephant handler; "Do you know that my brother has the same name as one of the Lions". "Does he now, which one is that" replied the Zoo Keeper.

"Luke" Hannah replied. "Is that so, little Luke is one of my favourite Lions here" the Keeper said. "We must be off now as it is almost time for Hannah here to have her lunch if you want to walk along with us you can watch her. It was only a short way to where the elephants feed so they both went along to see what Hannah the Elephant was having for her lunch. A member of the Safari Park staff was waiting for Hannah the Elephant to arrive before serving up her lunch of fine straw and a very large bowl of mixed fruit, bananas, Apples, Pears, Carrots, Lettuce and some Sugar Cane which would all be followed by gallons of water. "I hope you enjoy your day in the park, now say goodbye to Hannah" said the member of staff. Both Hannah and Luke said; "Goodbye Hannah" to the elephant before continuing on their tour. They were coming to the end of the Outdoor animals section and there was just one or two left to see.

They both liked the Giraffe and the Snow Leopard and Hannah was so sure that of all the animals the Snow Leopard should be able to talk to people.

But the snow Leopard must have had a long hard day because when Hannah asked him what his name was, he just gave a big yawn. Hannah thought that maybe it wasn't a good idea to talk to a Snow Leopard after all, so they made their way towards the Indoor animals. Then Luke said; "There is a Café over there, do you want an ice cream or something"? "No thank you but I will have a Coke please" said Hannah. She told Luke that he could meet her at the Sea lion section and as she entered the indoor section the first animals that Hannah saw were a Blue Poison Frog and two McCaws.

Hannah didn't find the bird section very interesting as all they seemed to do was make a lot of noise. She then headed towards a sign that said Marine section. "It's got to be better than this lot" Hannah thought as she went through the Aquatic area. This section did look more interesting and Hannah at once made her way to look at a young Seal". This is better," I have never seen a Seal of that colour before" Hannah thought. She went closer and then she heard herself saying "She's beautiful".

Then she turned to the Seal; "Hello, what's your name" Hannah said. The seal turned its head and looked at Hannah with her sad sorrowful eyes. "My name is Blondie, they call me that because of the colour of my fur" the seal said. "I knew the animals could talk" Hannah said, then moving closer she asked; "How long have you lived here"? "I have been here almost two years now" the young Seal replied. "Were you born in this Park?" Hannah asked. "No I was born on the East Coast not far from here" the Seal said. "How did you get in this place then"? Hannah wanted to know. "That's a long story, but if you come down here on the rocks and sit beside me I will tell you all about it" said the young Seal. When they had settled as comfortably as they could get on the rocks, the young Seal said to Hannah "As I told you I was born quite near to here on the East coast. My mother was very young when I was born. She was also very beautiful. She wanted to be the Queen of the North Sea I was just a burden to her. When I was only two weeks old she abandoned me and it was on a Christmas Day. With no one to look after me and teach me to catch fish and how to survive, I was helpless. I had no chance of surviving. Luckily I was washed up on the beach. It had been snowing for two days and I was hoping against hope that my mother would return to rescue me. But she had her own dreams and I was left to fend for myself. Fortunately for me a young couple came along the beach, they put me in a crate and took me to their home. They kept me in a Paddling Pool in a shed at the bottom of their garden. They fed me on Condensed Milk and Tuna fish. I got very sick. I cried every night, but no one came. Eventually someone must have heard me for the Authorities arrived one day and took me to an Animal Rescue Centre. I was kept there until I was well enough to be transferred here to this Park. I could not go back to the Sea I would not be able to survive, so this is my home now". Hannah felt very sad for the young seal, without a mother to look after her, "Do you like it here" she asks. "Yes I do I perform tricks for the children every day. They like me and I like them. Sometimes my trainer Albert lets the children give me a little piece of Chocolate as a treat and in return I always give of my best and make sure that I am never late for a performance" Blondie then said that she must go now as she had a rehearsal for the evening show so she said; "Goodbye Hannah, come back and see my show with your family" Hannah said that she would be back and that she would bring all her friends as well. The young seal then dived into the water and swam across to begin her practice session. Hannah caught a glimpse of Blondie as she made her way out of the building to see where Luke had got to. She was thinking that he had found a pinball machine or something like that in the Café and that was why he was so long getting her Coke. Then she heard someone calling; "Hannah......Hannah", when she opened her eyes she realised that it was her mother telling her that if she didn't get out of bed very soon she would not be going to the Safari Park today. Hannah got out of bed straight away, as she didn't want to miss the chance of seeing her friend Blondie again.

THE END...........

The Flying Bedsteads

Daniel   *David*

Daniel and David were twins and their parents had recently moved to a new house in a country village. It was time to change things like curtains, carpets and a new bed for each of the boys as they were almost ten years old and had just about out grown their old beds. They all went to the local bed store to find a pair of twin beds. Fairly soon they found a set that both the boys liked very much. Now all they had to do was find suitable mattresses for the beds. A short time later they had tried out every Mattress in the showroom. "This one's too soft," said Daniel. "This one's too wobbly," said David. "This one is far too hard," said mum. "This one is not wide enough David might fall out" Dad said. "Firm but not hard that's what we want" said Mum. "That's what we're really looking for somewhere between firm and hard." and so it went on until the owner of the bed store gave up and told them; "I'm afraid that's all we have you've seen every mattress that I have in stock" he said. Then he stroked his chin, "Except..." he paused. "No...no.... never mind" "Except for what"? Mum quickly inquired. The store keeper led them into a large room at the back of the shop and pulled away a white dust sheet. Underneath it were two single beds with mattresses on top. One was a silky Green mattress with gold stitching and Gold button studs which gleamed at them from amongst the old beds and boxes and other bits and pieces in the old stockroom. "Wow! What a beautiful mattress," said Daniel. "Lovely," gulped his Mum. The other one was a Gold mattress with Green stitching and Green button studs. "The mattresses need to be the same for the twins" said dad. "Well I like the Green one" Daniel said. "I like the Gold one" David told his father. "Do you not want the mattresses to be the same"? Mum asked the two boys. "It's all right to have trousers and jumpers the same but I would like my own mattress" replied Daniel. "That goes for me too". David said. "These mattresses look too good to sleep on and they are probably very expensive." said Dad. "No, not at all" the store keeper quickly said. "No, no. They are the cheapest pair in the shop even though both the beds and the mattresses were specially made. They were made by a Persian craftsman flown in specially to make them". He went on to explain that the complete beds and a carpet were ordered by an old gentleman who used to live in the old house behind the village Church, but the gentleman never ever came back to get them. "That's our house now we moved in there last week," said mum. "We want to buy our twin sons new beds" she said. "Daniel, climb onto that mattress" said his dad. "How is it Daniel. "Nice and comfy" asks Mum. "Owee! Oo.e It's as hard as a rock" said Daniel. "It makes all the other hard mattresses feel like feathers". "David you try the other mattress" said Dad. David lay down on the Gold mattress and he too thought the same as his twin brother Daniel that the mattress was too hard. Mum then said "Let's have another look at those in the show room again, they will probably feel quite different after this." As his mum and dad followed the store keeper back into the showroom, Daniel and David gazed at the Green and Gold mattresses. They were about to join their parents when a voice said: "You like my colours Daniel don't you". Both of the twins looked around but couldn't see anyone. "Who said that?" Daniel whispered. "I did," the voice said. "Over here in the corner" Daniel went back to where he had been standing and almost jumped out of his skin. "It's me Bertie The Flying Bedstead" the voice said. "You see I was ordered and made with this mattress and the other bed is my twin so we can't be separated, you both know what I mean being twins yourselves. The mattresses have got to be hard to fly properly in the wind. The man in the shop doesn't know what to do with us. Please buy the twin beds Daniel I and my twin brother Barney need to get out from under this dust sheet and get some fresh air, we need to spread our springs." Then Daniel said. "Bedsteads don't talk never mind fly." "Oh yes they do," replied Barney and in a second he was hovering four feet off the floor, his mattress colours glowing and twinkling like a flying merry-go-round. "How did you know my name"? Daniel asked. "I heard your father tell you to lie on the mattress, if your parents buy us we will take you and David for a spin' we will take you to anywhere you want to go." Barney said but when it had floated back to the floor Daniel and David had gone. Out in the showroom their mother and father were just about to buy a nice mattress when David said to his father. "You must buy the Gold and Green beds and mattresses daddy, you've got to. They are far better quality than the rest and there is also a carpet to match for our bedroom" His mum and dad were not very keen about the green and gold mattresses, but the store owner had a little smile on his face". Your son does have a very good point there Sir." Mum put her hand to her mouth thoughtfully. "It is half price does the price include the complete beds and the carpet". Mum asked the store keeper. "Yes indeed madam and a hard bed is usually recommended by most doctors and I can let you have the carpet to match all at half price." Mum nodded. "Have them delivered to the house behind the old Church by bedtime." said Daniel's father and Daniel saw that the shop owner gave a huge sigh of relief. "They will be there before you can say "Bats in the Belfry." "Bats....in...what"? replied mum. "Just a figure of speech Madam," said the store keeper and by the time they had all arrived at their home the beds, complete with the mattresses and the carpet, were already in the boy's bedroom. "How did they get that stuff here before us"? David asked his dad. "Nobody passed us in a delivery truck." Daniel said. David lay down on his bed with the Golden mattress. "This is the most comfortable bed I have ever had." He said.

"Beauty before bounce" came a little voice. "Who said that?" asks mum. "I…I did," said David quickly. "It was me I said it." "Let's have some tea and a sit down". Mum remarked to Dad. "Good idea I'll make it," offered dad and they all went downstairs and dad lit a fire in the old Victorian fireplace.

That night both boys were too excited to sleep. The house seemed to be full of new sounds and there were also far too many places to explore the next day. But best of all there was Bertie and Barney the Flying Bedsteads on which they was resting. Finally just as Daniel was falling asleep he heard a sound which he thought came from the upstairs hallway. "Pssst…Pssssst… Daniel…. Pssst," Slowly Daniel sat up his mattress began to glow and Bertie the Flying Bedstead said. "Let's go for a spin we can go anywhere you like". "Anywhere"? Daniel whispered. "Anywhere you want to go we were made for speed not comfort". Bertie told Daniel. "But what about mum and dad" replied Daniel? "They are asleep just name a place". "What about Barney and David"? Daniel said. David had woken up and he had heard most of the conversation between Bertie and Daniel. "My old teacher told us all about the highest mountain in the world: Mount Everest" he said. "Would you like to go to Mount Everest Daniel" Bertie asks. "I don't mind" answered Daniel. Instantly the huge bedroom window the one that Daniel and David had thought was so strange when they first arrived at the new house burst open. There was a bright flash and a swoosh of wind as Daniel and David were suddenly flying out into the night sky at what felt like the speed of Light on their twin Beds. But not just any beds, it was Bertie and Barney the Flying Bedsteads. As clouds shot past Bertie let out an excited scream like he was riding on a roller coaster and so did Daniel but only because Bertie did. David couldn't believe his eyes. The earth was below and the stars were above. Then in just moments the night had disappeared and they were in daytime again and in very bright sunshine. As Bertie and Barney bumped down to earth Daniel and David gasped and looked around. It took him some time to take it all in. David had to rub his eyes several times. There was no doubt about it; they were perched on the very top of a huge mountain covered in snow and ice. Daniel nervously dusted some snow off his little head. "Where are we?" he asked in a timid voice. "We are at Mount Everest twenty nine thousand and thirty five feet. The highest place on earth as requested". Barney said proudly. "I love this view thanks for choosing it" he said. Daniel stared at the wonderful sight. As far as the eye could see there were jagged Grey and White Mountains, the palest blue sky and air that made him dizzy to breathe. It was like being on another planet. Then something caught David's eye. It was a ring of frozen flags on the very top of the mountain. "What are those flags doing up here?" he asked. "They look like those old moon landing photos." Bertie said. "The Moon!" said Daniel who seemed a little confused but Mattie went on to explain that the many climbers who had scaled the highest mountain in the world had left their National Flags there, to prove that they had reached the top. David was too shocked to listen or speak and he thought that perhaps he should have asked to go somewhere like the park near their old house where he used to play with his friends that he had left behind when they had moved house. "Can we go home now please? It's chilly up here"? Asked Daniel as he lay down on his mattress and tried to keep warm, he had no idea that they were the first children ever to conquer Mount Everest on Flying Bedsteads. "We will have you two back in your room before you can say" "Bats in the Belfry"? "That is what the man in the bed shop said but I don't know why he said it." "Someday you'll find out Daniel". Said Bertie and in seconds they were flying back into the night sky again alongside Barney and David. Moments later with a flash and a thud they arrived in boy's bedroom. "Nice ride, eh"? Said Bertie "More than that," said Daniel. "Downright cold I'd say, I think I'm going to get warm. Thanks for the… you know… Well, good night Bertie". "Any time good night Daniel good night sleep well, your mum and dad are." And it was true his mum and dad were snoring in harmony just as they were before they had left for their flight to the top of the world, which had ended before you could say; "Bats in the Belfry".

Early the following morning, Daniel rubbed his eyes extra hard to make sure that the bed and his trip to Mount Everest were really a dream. But when he sat up in bed he was staring at his feet with a puzzled look. "How did I get snow all over my feet"? He thought as he quickly scooped the snow off and put his slippers on to save his toes from getting frostbitten.

By the end of their first Sunday breakfast at the old house the day was planned out. The boys could explore the old house, his Mum would decide what chores could be done in the garden and Dad would try and make sense of the kitchen equipment. At the days end everyone was exhausted and ready for bed even before it was dark. The old house behind the Church needed so much work doing to it that Daniel

112

could see that every weekend for a whole year would be spent on clearing and cleaning and scraping and painting and digging and fixing. But there was something very special about that old house. Very special indeed and Daniel was determined to find out everything about its history. He had so many questions in his mind for his Mum and Dad; it was easier for them to tell him to get to sleep than try to answer them as they themselves didn't really know the answer. "It's just an old house dear" mum had said. "All old houses are special. That's why we moved from our lovely house in the city but this is a lovely house too". David was not convinced by his Mum's enthusiasm for their almost crumbling new home. Dad didn't take part in any of the talks about the old house. This made Daniel wonder even more especially as Dad didn't talk about the old barn that was behind the house which he called the old coaching house and the door was kept locked with Pad Locks. That night Daniel and David lay awake for hours waiting for a voice to say "pssst,…. psssst, want to go for a spin" But nothing happened so finally they both fell asleep and Daniel had a nightmare about his new school which he was to start in a few days' time. He dreamt that nobody liked him and they all laughed at him whenever he tried to answer the teacher's questions. That night was no fun at all.

As soon as his Mum Dad and David were dressed and had gone down the stairs to prepare for breakfast, Daniel knelt down on the carpet between his bed and David's bed. "What happened"? He asked, but there was no answer. "Bertie are you there"? Still there was no reply. Daniel sighed heavily and left his room. But just as he was about to go down to the kitchen he heard a low "pssst…psssst" and ran back. "It takes a lot of energy to fly to Mount Everest even a mattress and a bed has to sleep" yawned Bertie. "Just carry on I'll let you know when we can take another spin." said Bertie and Daniel beamed a big smile. "Thank goodness for that. I thought you were just a dream. Or I was imagining things, or even a Mir…" he almost said 'a miracle, but didn't. "I think I've got the point Daniel and no I am none of those things nor am I a miracle. I just need to recharge my batteries by doing what mattresses and beds do all day, sleep. Then we'll go wherever your imagination wants to take you. Before you can say…" "Bats in the belfry," laughed Daniel.

Two nights later Daniel found himself being woken up again, "Pss…..pss …psssst…..Daniel" said the whispered voice. Bertie was ready for another spin, "Where to"? Bertie asked, "To the park where all my old friends play". Replied Daniel and within seconds all four of them were once again shooting through the night sky through the clouds and across a hundred counties, shortly to land next to the swings in the park where the twin brothers once lived. "Where is everybody"? Asked David, "They are all in bed it's still night time here". Daniel hung his head. "I wanted to see my friends again" he said "Don't worry you'll make new friends. Change can be hard but once you get used to it, you will find all sorts of new things to make up for the things you left behind. Believe me I know" said Bertie. Daniel nodded but he wasn't at all sure. "Moving house is like going to another planet and just as lonely." Barney then started to tremble with excitement. "That's it another planet are you ready David" " I'm not ready for the Moon or Mars yet. I'm just a beginner at this sort of thing." said David sitting up straight on the mattress as his bed rose slowly into the sky. He stared down at the town where he was born and brought up until the day that he had to move. It looked so different from above not how he remembered it. Then Bertie said: "Anyway who mentioned the Moon, I was thinking about Jupiter. But Its just that we need to get fresh air after so many years in the furniture shop that's all." With that Bertie then made a slow fly past of the town hovering for a moment over the boy's old house. "How did you know that was our old house and how to find my old playground in our old town"? asked Daniel. "All in good time Daniel. All in good time" Bertie said as he made a sharp turn west. "Maybe we should head home and as for the planets, they have been around for a while they can wait a bit longer for us". Daniel and David took a final sad look at their old house and then they were gone.

The nightmare that Daniel had about his new school, was not a nightmare at all instead it was all true. The class was half the size of the one he was used to, but the kids were nowhere near as friendly. It took Daniel ages to make friends at his old school and then his Mum and Dad had decided to move house without any real explanation. It just didn't seem fair. Daniel was fed up at having to start over again and fed up with being an outcast until it suited people to like him. As his teacher introduced him to the other children not one of them smiled, but instead somebody threw a ball of paper which hit him squarely on the nose and the teacher did nothing. Daniel noted that this was not a good sign. The days at school passed very slowly, but soon most of the children got bored with making fun of Daniel's name, or teasing him about the funny old house where he lived, or just ignoring him as if he was invisible, which was one of their favourite games. Unfortunately what they did not get bored with was laughing at him when he couldn't answer the teacher's questions. Questions like: "What do you call the red hot river that flows from a volcano Daniel". When Daniel replied that it was called magma everybody laughed, including the teacher, who said he had never heard of such a word and it was called lava. The laughter seemed to echo around the classroom and Daniel felt even more unpopular and lonely in a school that he never wanted to go to in the first place. "They think they're so clever," Daniel told his Mum and Dad when he got home. "And when I asked them how high Mount Everest is none of them knew the answer but I did". "All children are like that Daniel" said Mum as she served him a plate of stew that looked just like a plate of red hot magma. "Things will get better you'll see, I promise". His dad looked at him over the rim of his glasses. "How high is Mount Everest"? He asked Daniel. "I've often wondered, haven't you, mum"? Daniel looked at the plate of 'lava', then at his mum and dad. "You don't know how high Mount Everest is?" Dad pulled a face as if he knew more than just how high it is. But his mum smiled and said: "Are you going to laugh at us for not knowing the answer Daniel?" "No," said Daniel. "No. It's just that... I mean, I... have... you know...." But he knew that he couldn't come out and say that he and his new bedstead were at the very summit of the highest mountain on earth only a few days before. So he just said: "Twenty nine thousand and thirty five feet". Later that night after Mum and Dad went to bed and started snoring Bertie told Daniel how to deal with his new classmates. "If they don't know what magma is then we will just have to show them Daniel" as they shot out through the huge window without even asking him where he wanted to go. "Although," Bertie had added in mid-flight "Be prepared for them not to believe a word of what you say, specially the teacher. Teachers hate to be wrong because they're supposed to be right about almost everything which they are not." As they zoomed above the earth and vast expanses of ocean

Daniel lay with his head poking over what he guessed was Bertie's shoulder. As usual in what seemed like seconds they were dropping down through the clouds just as Daniel remembered from aeroplane trips, to Spain and other places with his parents, before coming in to land. Only this time it wasn't Malaga or Madrid. When the clouds began to clear Daniel gasped at what he saw. It was sunrise and they were flying at great speed above a vast hole in the top of a mountain with stinky smoke rising slowly into the orange sky. Yes it had to be it was a live volcano, exactly like the one his teacher taught him about. "Where are we"? Daniel asked. "Mount Vesuvius the Hottest place on earth" replied Bertie and suddenly he tipped them downwards at such a steep angle that Daniel thought that he might slide off and fall through the thick smoke to fry in hot magma. He held on so tightly that his knuckles turned white. "I hope you brought the ash bucket and tongs from the fireplace" said Bertie as he inched them next to bubbles of oozing orange rock. "Be quick Daniel my fringes are heating up." said Bertie. "Yes I did bring the bucket and I'm ready" said Daniel. "Pick out a nice red-hot piece of magma, drop it in the bucket and we'll be on our way." Daniel wiped the sweat from his brow. This was the most thrilling thing he had ever done in his life so far and he was beginning to like it a lot. "You had better be careful," said Bertie in the early hours of the same morning. "If your mum and dad get up and find volcanic ash on your bed sheets they might begin to suspect something". He told Daniel. "I think we should use the vacuum cleaner with the brush attached it's in the garage." Daniel said as he edged his way past a beat up old Austin Seven that his father used to tinker with. He unclipped the old vacuum cleaner from its charging bracket and went back to vacuum down the sheets that were covered in the very same volcanic ash that destroyed a place called Pompeii in A.D. 79, which was something his teacher was right about.

The following morning Daniel's teacher stared at the piece of warm rock in Daniel's ash bucket and laughed. "You and I might know what magma is Daniel, but the rest of the class calls it lava. I do appreciate you bringing in a piece of hot coal from your old fireplace to make your point." Daniel was devastated. Not only did his teacher not know what magma was all along but he believed that the teacher thought magma was a bit of half burned coal from the fire. "There is one good thing," said Bertie when Daniel told him what had happened later that night. "And what is that"? Daniel asked. "At least the whole class wasn't there to laugh at you". Bertie replied.

Weeks went by and Daniel's new home was beginning to look more like a normal house and less like the Adams Family mansion. There was new paint on the doors and windows, the grass was cut, hedges were trimmed and when he wasn't up in the old coach house doing something he refused to talk about Daniel's Dad was on the roof fixing the weather vane or tending to his gooseberry patch. Daniel's Mum spent many hours in her makeshift Home Office trying to work at her computer but all she could do was complain about how cold it was. It was so cold and icy that first winter in the country, Daniel wished he could wake his mum up on a trip to the Sahara Desert where she could warm up. He and David also wished that they could share the secret of their bedsteads with their parents. It was a lot to keep bottled up for just two little boys and they missed the company of their old friends really badly. But they were miles away in what felt like another land; another life. The winter passed and soon the summer holidays would start. The boys dreaded the thought. Unless they made friends soon his whole summer would be spent helping Dad to fix up the house. So the next time that they were invited to go for a spin, Daniel and David said that they just wanted to sit and talk. Bertie and Barney were their only true friends and they agreed that travelling at the speed of light wasn't always the best thing if you needed a chat, so they talked. For bedsteads Bertie and David were very wise individuals and full of good advice that the two boys listened to, but after a while they pleaded with to be dropped off at the park so that they could play with all their old friends like before. Barney sighed and in a very sad voice he said: "We can't do that, because to take you to the ends of the earth, or even your old playground, means that we will have to tell your parents. That's how it works and it's the only way it works."

Daniel was unable to contain his disappointment. "How can they protect me when they're asleep"? Said Daniel, but Barney knew how it felt to be alone. "Even when they're asleep they know you're here Daniel", Bernie said trying to sound positive. "That's the special thing about mums and dads, not that we should tell them about me and Barney you understand. It's still our secret." "Yes but how do we make new friends nobody at school likes us because we are strangers and there isn't another boy or girl around here of our age group for miles." Bertie gave a little chuckle. "I have an idea that might just work Daniel. It's all about being straight and telling the truth and with a little help from a friend of course".

During the next few days while he was on his school lunch break the two most popular children in their class came over to Daniel and David. At first Daniel thought they were going to tease or bully him but one of them Andrew, looked him straight in the eye; "My Dad says magma is what mostly comes out of volcanoes he says that it is Molten rock under the earth's surface. Lava is stuff that flows from the volcano and becomes solid when it cools" He wanted to know how Daniel knew that when their teacher didn't know it. David attempted a smile but nobody smiled back. But the fact that they were even talking to the twins was a good start, so he explained: "We went to Mount Vesuvius in Italy and saw with our own eyes that's how". It was far too complicated to explain that really their teacher did know and so did he even before going to Vesuvius. The kids didn't know what to say but they didn't laugh. The other school friend Janice said: "You're weird David." Daniel thought this was definitely a good sign. Being weird was better than being alone and he was sure that this was a turning point for them at school. He was about to explain that he was able to travel all over the world on his magic bedstead but decided to say that he went to places in his sleep instead. It was too soon to tell them about the bedsteads; they would only laugh. But they burst out laughing anyway and Janice tossed a ball of paper at Daniel hitting him squarely on the forehead. "That hurt," said Daniel angrily nevertheless he was glad to discover who it was who throws the paper. "Okay. I'll prove it." Daniel said to them. "Name something from anywhere in the world and I'll have it in class by tomorrow morning." Janice seemed impressed. She made a face as though she was thinking very deeply and then said: "Got it! Get me a poison dart from a tribe of Indians in the Amazon Rain Forest". "No problem" said David casually brushing some invisible fluff from his shoulder. "Anything else madam"? He inquired. "Oh also a piranha in a Jam jar while you're at it". Andrew said. Once again they all laughed but it was a different laughter than before and Daniel could tell because this time he didn't care if they laughed. They were hooked so Daniel and David got up and walked off. Barney was right it was all about being straight and telling the truth however weird the truth may seem. That night The Magnificent Four were once again hurtling through the skies at the speed of light. "Are you sure this is safe"? Daniel asked Bertie as they flew low across the waters of the Amazon River. "Safe as houses but keep your head down." Daniel wasn't so sure. Then just as he gazed down at the dark green river snaking its way through the never ending rain forest there was a loud thud to Bertie's left side. "Woow I think we've just found your poisoned dart." Bertie was right Daniel carefully pulled the small brown dart from Bertie's left side. "Don't worry it didn't hurt" Bertie said as they climbed away from the river bank. "How are we going to get the piranha fish" said David. "Did you bring the bacon rasher "? Ask Barney. "Yes" Daniel replied. At another bend in the river Bertie came to within inches of the water to let Daniel hang his fishing hook over the side. In seconds Daniel had caught not one but two piranhas on a single piece of bacon that would normally be sitting on his breakfast plate. Quick as a flash Daniel then plopped the fish in a Jam jar and closed the lid. The next morning breakfast was strange as Mum made a comment to Dad about losing her favourite large Jam Jar. But all that his father said was: "Good place for fish if you don't want to lose a finger." Daniel thought this was an odd remark although he was too excited to read anything into it.

At school break Janice and Andrew cornered the twin brothers again in the playground. They were about to have more fun at their expense when Daniel produced the poison dart and David a piranhas in the jam jar. The others were speechless. Daniel smiled and walked away. Just as Bertie had promised everything suddenly changed for him. He and David were now popular ones in the classroom. It was like a big heavy door had just opened. They were no longer outcasts. They had a special secret and everybody wanted to know them because of it. When school closed for the summer Janice and Andrew came to the old house almost every day and Daniel and David were having such fun that they completely forgot about the friends they had left behind when they moved to the old house behind the Church. Keeping their secret for now was the hardest part but it was well worthwhile. "As long as you two bedsteads are in the house we will always have friends to play with," Daniel told Bertie one night, but he didn't expect the reply that he got. "You don't need us any more Daniel." "What do you mean of course we need you" said Daniel. He draped his arm over Mattie's corner the bit that he thought was his shoulder. "I want my friends to meet you and go for a spin"? Bertie didn't answer right away it was as though he had been thinking things over. "Perhaps one day, maybe Daniel. But right now you both must rely on who you are to your friends, not how you can impress them through me. All I did was help you break the ice. That's all. Don't forget that Janice and Andrew came to your house to play. You didn't go to them." "How do you know that?" asked Daniel looking puzzled. "You have never seen them and you even know their names as well"? "All in good time Daniel, all in good time. All I'm saying is that Janice and Andrew wanted to be friends with you all along but didn't know how to." "But, but " Daniel was about to say something when Bertie stopped him "This old house has so many strange and exciting places to play that even adventures with Flying Bedsteads will seem dull by comparison. Use your imagination. Look in the old coach house if you don't believe me"? Bertie told him. That night Daniel went back to his room feeling confused as if he'd lost a best friend. But he hadn't. Bertie and Barney were the best friends he could ever have; even if he and his brother didn't know it yet. The next day when Janice and Andrew came over to play David pleaded with his Dad to let them play in the old coach house. But Dad just said: "All in good time son. All in good time", as he checked that all the doors and windows were firmly locked before hiding the keys. Somehow, this didn't matter to Daniel. He just showed his friends the tunnel in the basement and the old tree house in the woods and the secret room in the attic where his Dad stored his gooseberry jam. It didn't matter to Janice or Andrew either. They'd found a pair of new friends. Even if they were a bit weird sometimes and things around the house behind the old Church didn't always make sense. That summer holiday was the best one that David and Daniel ever had. They were so tired at the end of each day that they didn't even notice that Bertie and Barney were no longer calling "Pssssst,….Daniel… Pssst,…David." as soon as his mum and dad had fallen asleep. And of course Mattie was right. Daniel's imagination was just as much fun and sometimes just as scary as trips on The Flying Bedstead. How could bedsteads be so wise? Soon it was into the autumn and school had long since started again. One evening David awakened in the middle of the night. He could hear a familiar hissing sound. He smiled to himself. It had been a long time, what felt like a lifetime; so much had changed. Of course, the hissing sound was Mattie. Who else could it be? "Pssst. Psssssst. David… want to go for a Spin"?

Without looking up David whispered;

"Hello Barney"?

He popped up from the covers as his dad was saying;

"Would you like to go for a spin David."

The End………

A

Selection

of

Rhymes

The loyal Fans

The League kicked off in August full of fresh new **hope**
It took us into December, to reach that slippery **slope**
So now it's back to that league where we have just **been**
This season is the worst one that we have ever **seen**
We all have got our memories not all of them are **bad**
But the lack of one good striker drove lots of us quite **mad**
There was Armagh, Coleraine and Glentoran **too**
Glenavon and The Swifts to name you just a **few**
Newry town and Derry were the only games we **won**
Yet there were other games when we could not hold **on**
Cliftonville, at Limavady gave an awesome **display**
With Fulton on his own, he kept more goals at **bay**
Portadown was dreadful Dungannon that was **worse**
At least at Ballymena we managed to score our **first**
At Lisburn it was freezing and Crusaders was very **wet**
Donegal was costly when Smithy's penalty missed the **net**
I lost count of all the players used throughout the **year**
Jones he went to Linfield and loads of them came **here**
Contracts they were broken but nothing could really **stop**
The wage cuts the Gate receipts and the inevitable **drop.**
So finally it all ended on March day number **eight**
The day that Donegal Celtic really sealed our **fate**
So what about the future now I really do not **know**
Some players they may stay here but I'm guessing most will **go**
But whatever point of view we have as fans we have one **aim**
And that's to stand up and be proud of Larne FC once **again.**

That Blasted Mobil Phone

One moment I was fast **asleep**
Then suddenly I woke to my mobile's **bleep**
I fumbled around to answer but **instead**
To my horror the phone it fell under my **bed**
The bleeps I could hear but no phone could I **see**
All the time I was wondering who can this **be**
I glanced at the clock it was now **2am**
I thought to myself shall I bother with **them**
I carried on fumbling hanging over the **side**
While my arm it was searching far and **wide**
At last I could feel the smooth touch of the **phone**
By this time I was lying flat out at the **prone**
I opened the case to find who it was **calling**
It opened the wrong way as I felt the phone **falling**
This time it fell at the wall side of my **bed**
I just lay in the dark listening to every word **said**
"Are you there sweetheart" I could hear someone **say**
The words I might welcome another time of the **day**
I tried one more time to get that damn **phone**
But when I retrieved it the Voice it had **gone**
The lesson to learn from this tale of **mine**
Switch on your bed lamp and all will be **fine.**

We Oul Codgers

We're sitting on a Welcome we meet when the weather's **fine**
There's Ted an' Dave, an' 'Nev and Me all sitting here in **line**
And for us dear oul' codgers life holds no greater **boon**
Than sit and watch the Golfers play on a sunny **afternoon**
Some folk meet in snooker halls some congregate in **pubs**
While others meet to gossip in expensive Country **clubs**
But we prefer our Welcome may that seat be always **warm**
And may the gods be ever kind and keep us from all **harm**
At times Nev suffers with a cough my chest it'll start to **wheeze**
The wind comes up the Seventh Tee and soon becomes a **breeze**
At times rheumatics bother us because old age is **there**
Our joints are kin' o' rusty now and long beyond **repair**
In spite of this we're sitting here these loyal friends and **I**
The criac is good just like it should as other golfers hurry **by**
Everyone's been staring they just can't believe our **play**
They haven't seen a team shoot a round like ours all **day**
Nev played out of the rough with shots we couldn't **believe**
His putting's been much better than he ever could **conceive**
The Bunkers hold no sway o'er Dave he blasts his way right **out**
With every wondrous shot he makes he gives a victory **shout**
As Ted draws back and makes a putt we watch the ball go **in**
We can't believe how wonderful his playing here has **bin**
But we shot a sixty-five today and can't believe it's **so**
Especially as we leave the green with only fifteen holes to **go**
When next you cross the Second Tee and see us sitting **there**
Perhaps you'll pass the time of day and ask us how we **fare.**

Going home to Larne.

My Childhood days often come to me and stir inside my **brain**.
So would you like to come with me as I stroll down memory **lane**
In dreams I still return to my home **Town**
To visit childhood haunts and walk **around**
They start when I was a boy of **four**
The time, our country went to **war**
The Prime Minister of the **day**
Came on the radio to **say**
Britain is at war this September **day**
We knew our dads were going **away**
They told us 'Dig for victory' 'Make do and **mend'**
They were so silly slogans as we had nought to **spend**
So off to the War dad had to **go**
When he'd return we'd never **know**
Uncles Joe, George, John and Cousin **Jack**
Joined up like Dad and didn't came **back**
One night before we went to **bed**
The night sky turned a ruby **red.**
This was a night in the Belfast **blitz**
When many people were blown to **bits**
Then one Tuesday it was the 8th.of **May**
Europe got some peace they called it VE **day**
It was over now after more than five long **years**
What cost we'll never know in people's blood and **tears**
Can you remember the town of Larne as once it used to **be**
The Laharna Hotel in between the Town Hall and the **Quay**
And tell me now do you recall that one-time railway **track**
That used to run from Station Road to Ballyclare and **back**
The streets and roads had names .like Recreation and **Waterloo**
The Old Pavilion Ballroom and the Regal Cinema **too**

Shipbuilding at the Harbour then Televisions there from **Pye**
Were all a part of dear old Larne in days now long gone **by**
The GPO in Main Street the Fishermen in the **Bay**
The Meetinghouse at Mill Street where tall flats stand **today**
The Noggy Burn, Gege Mill and also Coopers **Lane**
Were all a part of old Larne we'll never see **again**
Can you remember Larne and then recall the **scene**
When every year the Summer Fair was held at Bleach **Green**
The Railway Station had two platforms yes it's **true**
And in Circular Road we had a new Bus Station **too**
And what about the Hospital the Workhouse and Trow **Lane**
The avenue in the Roddens that was once Mc Garel's **domain**
The Olderfleet Hotel, and the fish sold on the **Pier**
These were all a part of Larne and memories I hold **dear**
So many are the memories of landmarks once I knew
Longmore's, Dorman's, the Mourne and the King's Arms **too**
The Woolworth Store in Main Street the Church at Black's **Lane**
They were all a part of Larne we'll never see **again**
The Narrow Gauge behind the green and of course Mill **Lane**
These were all a part of Larne we'll never see **again**
But I said farewell to dear old Larne and a girl I did **adore**
I never kissed her cheek again never held her hand no **more**
I knew that I had lost her love no joy was there for **me**
To seek my future somewhere else in a land across the **sea**
I hadn't got much money then misfortune was just part of my **lot**
And there were those who said to me Larne's just as well **forgot**
But I never forget I'm a Larne man and I'll never run **away**
So I vowed that in the future I'd return again one **day**
I remember leaving Old England far **behind**
Thoughts of my home coming for ever on my **mind**
It was a lovely sight from the ship I was on **board**
To see those Chimneys looming at **Ballylumford.**
I came back to my homeland the place of my **birth**
At last I was in Larne Lough and not the Solway **Firth**

I wandered to my old school yard where once I used to **play**
But that was in the days before foreign lands called me **away**
Running home in pouring rain down the Fair Hill steps I'd **flee**
Those were happy days in many ways in the Larne of '**43**
I still remember from those days where I was running **to**
It was to dear old Mill Street at number twenty **two**
And this was just the very place where I had spent my **youth**
And I was sad to leave it if you want to know the **truth**
The R.C Church where once I knelt to **pray**
Looked to me the very same as on my wedding **day**
At Mc Kenna School I sat on the **wall**
I knew every stone I had walked them **all**
That boundary wall with now no **flowers**
That school where I spent many happy **hours**
Along the Pound Street I make my **way**
Past the old library of **yesterday**
As I looked down Mill Street I could only **see**
Those tall old houses as they used to **be**
McGarel's corner shop and Jimmy Lees's **store**
Mossey Close's pub with its ever open **door**
I get at last to my old home my dream it is now **done**
As I look up at the window panes that reflect the setting **sun.**

A

Selection

Of

Golf

Yarns

A husband and wife were out playing golf. They teed off and one drive goes to the right and one drive goes to the left. The wife finds her ball in a patch of buttercups. She grabs a club and takes a mighty swing at the ball. She hits a beautiful shot, but in the process she hacks the hell out of the buttercups.

Suddenly a woman appears out of nowhere, dressed in a white robe. She blocks the golfer's path to her golf bag and looks at her and says, "I am Mother Nature and I don't like the way you treated the buttercups. From now on you won't be able to stand the taste of butter. Each time you eat butter you will become physically ill to the point of total nausea." The mystery woman then disappears as quickly as she had appeared.

Shaken, the wife calls out to her husband "Where is your ball?"
"It's over here in the pussy willows." The husband replies.
The wife screams back;
"For goodness sake don't hit that ball".

A young man called Fred went to work in another town. Fred was a keen golfer and some of his new work colleagues played golf every Saturday morning at the local Pay and Play Golf Course. Fred made inquiries and found that there was a space for him to play in a four ball every week if he wished to make it a definite commitment. Fred said that he would be there every Saturday morning but, on the odd occasion he may be fifteen minutes late.

On the first Saturday Fred was there on the first tee at 8.50 am ready for the tee off time which was always 9am for his playing partners. This group always played for money and that first day Fred won and collected his winnings from the other three players.

The next week Fred warned his playing companions that he may be fifteen minutes late on Saturday morning. However he turned up with plenty of time to spare before the appointed tee time. On this occasion Fred elected to play left handed and he again won and collected his winnings.

The same pattern emerged for several weeks with Fred saying that he might be fifteen minute late, but turning up in good time and playing left handed or right Handed and still collecting the spoils.

His playing companions were getting a bit fed up with Fred saying that he might be fifteen minutes late, then turning up and playing with both hands and winning the money. One of them asks Fred;

"How come you say every week that you might be late on Saturday morning yet turn up early and play with either hand Fred?" The other two players also wanted to know his answer.

Fred thought for a minute then he said; "I am a very superstitious person and every Saturday morning when I wake up I look to see what side my wife is sleeping on.

If she is sleeping on her right side I will play right Handed and if she is sleeping on her left side I will play left Handed".

His mates were intrigued by Fred's explanation and one of them asks; "What if she is lying on her back".

Fred looked him in the eye and said;
"That's when I'll be Fifteen minutes late".

A businessman and the local priest are out for a game of golf one day. The businessman was a high handicapper at the game and every time he missed a shot or a short putt he would shout "Shit".

The game went on and after several outbursts from the business man the priest could hold his tongue no longer. "Don't swear like that" he told his playing partner, "or God will punish you".

The man apologized and the game continued. As soon as he missed another shot he shouted "Shit" and continued to do this every time he missed a shot for the next few holes.

The priest was starting to get really angry by now and said "I must insist that you stop swearing otherwise God will hear and he may punish you!" But again, his pleas made no difference as the business man missed an easy putt on the seventeenth green and shouted "Shit".

Immediately the heavens parted and a bolt of lightning flew from the sky, hitting the priest who fell stone dead on the Green. Almost at once a booming voice was heard in the clouds,

"Shit I missed him."

A man is stranded on an island, all alone for several years. One day a gorgeous looking woman wearing a wet scuba suit arrives at the island.

She comes up to the chap and says, "How long has it been since you had a cigarette?" "A few years!" he answers. She reaches over, unzips the waterproof pocket on her left sleeve and pulls out a pack of cigarettes. He takes one, lights it, takes a long drag and says, "That was good!" Then she asks,

"How long has it been since you had a whisky?" He replies, "Several years!" She again reaches over, unzips her waterproof pocket on the right, pulls out a bottle of whiskey and gives it to him. He takes a long swallow and says,

"Wow that was fantastic!" Then she starts unzipping this long zipper that runs down the front of her wet suit as she says to him, "And how long has it been since you had some real fun?" The startled man replies,

"Good God, don't tell me you've got a set of golf clubs in there"…

A couple decide to go golfing to the best golf course in their County. While playing the husband tells his wife to be very careful, as there were many houses along the golf course. But the wife hooks one of her tee shots and it breaks a window pane of the biggest house at the course. The husband and wife decided to go and apologize to the owner of the house. When they reached the house they found a glass bottle lying on the floor broken into hundreds of pieces. They also found an old man sitting in his rocking chair who invited the couple inside.

The old man said, "I am a genie and I would like to thank you for setting me free from this bottle and I would like to grant you two wishes; but the third wish is mine." The husband says;

"I want a private aircraft for myself."
The wife said that she would like a house in every Capital City in Europe.

The genie said, "For the past 200 years I have not had sex and would like to have sex with the lady." The husband agrees and the genie takes the lady up stairs. Then he asks the lady;

"How old is your husband?" she replies "47"
The genie says;

"47 And he still believes in genies?"............

A golfer stood over his tee shot, looking up, looking down, measuring the distance, figuring the wind direction and speed and generally driving his playing partner nuts. Finally his partner says;

"Hit the damn ball will you".
The player answers;

"My wife is up there on the clubhouse veranda watching me. I want to make this a perfect shot."

"Well, bloody hell you don't stand a snowball in hell's chance of Hitting her from here" replied the irate golfer...............

Paddy came to work one day limping something awful. One of his fellow workers Reggie noticed this and asked Paddy what happened. "Oh nothing it's just an old Golf injury that acts up every so often." Paddy replied.

"I never knew you played golf" said Reggie.

"I don't I hurt it a couple of years ago when I lost £100 on the British Open play off.

I put my foot through the television." replied Paddy ....

During my brief stays in England in my earlier years I tried my hand at fishing in several rivers but mainly in the River Trent. I don't know why I bothered maybe it was for peace and quiet by the riverside like when I was a boy trying to fish in the Inver River.

A would be fisherman

I waited a moment to settle my **nerve**
Then made my cast with a right handed **curve**
The Fly settled down and the float it looked **good**
The trout then refused it as I figured it **would**
I lengthened the tippet before my next **try**
I changed my position and also the **fly**
I checked my rod for a good **presentation**
Then held my breath in great **anticipation**
The fly floated gently on its way to the **trout**
I knew this one would "take it" there was no **doubt**
I get all charged up and ready to **strike**
The float passes by something's still not **right**
Then I see a trout rise to an unknown **fly**
My heart starts to thump is it any wonder **why**
I try once again I'd done the best that I **can**
Before I realised that I am no **fisherman**

How

We

Lived

During

The

War

I would not attempt to visualise how our Victorian Ancestors lived but I know that conditions were very harsh. I do however know what it was like to live in Larne in the 1930s and 1940s during the War years. Our house in Mill Street was a three up and two down, but there were eleven people living there. Not much privacy and with no running water inside the house, chores like washing and Bath nights were difficult times. Just about everything was rationed during the War and many things for several years after that. Things like clothes and footwear most of us had only the one set or pair. Even if we had the money to buy more, we couldn't buy just anything without our Ration coupons; if they were used up we would have to acquire them on the "Black Market" or go without. To give some idea of the living conditions then, I have composed a few verses that will illustrate what it was like. Though it was no laughing matter during the war years, I have tried to be as humorous as I can to accurately tell the way it was.

Our House.

We didn't live in an Avenue a Close or in a **Way**
But in a Street where there was little room to **play**
Three rooms up and two down where we had to sleep and **eat**
And with eleven people in the house that was quite a **feat**
In these three bedrooms we all slept and life was very **hard**
More so as we only had one toilet in the **yard**
We never had a bath as such of this some may **recall**
It was six feet long and made of zinc and hung up on the **wall**
Bath nights for me were awful one of my worst **fears**
Aunt Sarah had long finger nails when washing out my **ears.**
She usually scrubbed my back as well it made me feel quite **sick**
Instead of using just a cloth I'm sure she used a **brick**
We didn't have much of anything just simple things and **yet**
We were eternally grateful for what little we could **get**
We never had a wardrobe in which our clothes were **kept**
The shirt we wore on the day was the one in which we **slept**
Hand me downs that were too big and came up to our **chin**
With big holes in old leather boots that let the water **in**
Times were really hard then and no matter what anyone **says**
I think they must be off their heads to call them good old **days**

Gas Mask, Identity Card and Middens

We all had an identity card we had a gas mask **too**
Nasty horrible things they were stuck to your face like **glue**
It was a daily ritual to practice wearing that **mask**
We all hated doing it as it was quite an awkward **task**
The Teacher came around to see that it was fitting **snug**
By pulling at the head strap with a fairly hefty **tug**
The idea was that these would keep us all **alive**
But if we had to wear them long would we indeed **survive**
We were glad when it finally stopped as a daily **routine**
But still we had to carry them no matter where we'd **been**
We always had to carry them even to the **loo**
But when the War it ended they disappeared from **view**
Can you remember during the war when times were really **hard**
Ration books and gas masks and the Midden down the **yard**
The whole Lane had the problem it wasn't just us you **know**
If you had to "go" you had to trudge through the rain or **snow**
We would light a little candle because all lights were **banned**
The way to stop it blowing out was to shield it with your **hand**
We would go off down the garden and then without a **doubt**
Just as we reached the Midden door the wind would blow it **out.**

Larne at Christmas 1943.

No lamps shone in Larne then no lights in windows **glowed**
The countryside and town were dark in every street and **road**
But when a frost was in the air the moon and stars shone **forth**
The constellations all were clear with Polaris to the **North**
There was no rush to spend and spend as is now the **fashion**
For many things that we might want were strictly on the **ration**
So what we couldn't buy we made with great **determination**
Paper chains from Larne Times strips we'd paint for **decoration**
But some did have a Christmas tree with no electric **lights**
They used small coloured candles in reds and greens and **whites**
These candles had a real live flame with no safety **regulations**
Never have I heard a case of Christmas tree **conflagrations**
As Christmas day was approaching no presents were in **sight**
It wasn't safe for Santa Claus to travel during the war at **night**
That's what Aunt Sarah told me and my younger **brother**
No stockings hung for Christmas just comforting each **other**
The Mill Lane pump provided water for a cup of Rosie **Lee**
Aunt Sarah said we wouldn't survive without our Lipton's **tea**
My fervent hope it won't happen again to future **generations**
Who get on with their everyday lives no need for **celebrations**

One night when I was a teenager I went to the Regal Cinema in Larne with some of my school pals. It was during the Blackout and an incident occurred concerning an old guy who used to live beside us in Mill Street then. The story is possibly best told like this;

The Courting Couple

It was way back in the war years in nineteen forty **three**
When an incident it took place that today still tickles **me**
Everything then was rationed and water was precious **too**
It had to be used very sparingly even when we used the **loo**
I happened to make my way home when I was just **thirteen**
I said Ta Ta to my young pals at the Regal where we'd **been**
I saw a couple who were under next door's bedroom **window**
The old man shouted out to them and told them where to **go**
But the courting got quite noisy the old man got **irate**
He shouted down to them "Clear off it's getting very **Late**"
But the couple just ignored him the old man Red he **saw**
"Are you going to shift" he said "Or do I call the **law?**"
The couple they just carried on oblivious to the old man's **plea**
But what then happened next was a complete surprise to **me**
The old man opened his window a bucket in his **hand**
He tipped the contents over them just where they did **stand**
The couple stopped abruptly as the girl shouted out in **dismay**
"I'll get the law on you old man wasting water in this **way**
I have a mind to call the police and have you put in **jail**
Wasting precious water from that rusty **pail**"
The old man was not bothered by this menacing **threat**
As he waved his fist at the couple standing there all **wet**
"I told you twice to clear off so now you know" said **he**
"That wasn't water in the Pail it happens to be my **Pee**"

My home town of Larne never suffered from any bombing or War damage, but that didn't stop me from wondering what might have been. This is how I imagine Larne heroes coping with the War.

Our Larne Town Heroes

After the War great tales were told of heroes who were **unafraid**
So let me tell what we befell on the night of Our Towns **raid**
A Tomcat growled, a tabby howled Aunt Sarah's hens had **fits**
The Cows bawled and mares foaled the night of our Towns **blitz**
A mangy old dog went streaking past which no one could **pursue**
A warden cried as the dog he espied "It could win the **waterloo"**
Out from his bed a warden sped as bombs fell round the **houses**
A hand he used to put out fires the other to hold up his **trousers**
Said Joe to Sal don't cry my love we'll be together in death or **life**
Light of a flare made Joe stare he was holding another man's **wife**
A young girl went dashing out to extinguish an incendiary's **flame**
Her elastic ripped down they slipped she carried on just the **same**
Our football goalie became a Hero at the height of five feet **three**
When he saw a falling land mine coming he headed it into the **sea**
Many other strange things went on in Larne town that **night**
Only the man in the moon could see so he keeps his secrets **tight**
So in the future years to come when I am laid to **rest**
My kids can tell their kids how Our Town stood the **test**

Our old school master was Bertie Fulton an Irish International footballer. He played for Larne FC and Belfast Celtic and gained over forty caps. He also was a member of the Great Britain Football team in the 1936 Olympic Games in Berlin. He coached our school team when we won the Irish Schools Cup. I was proud to be a member of that victorious team. This poem is to Bertie.

An Ode to Bertie Fulton

I saw a phantom figure he was high up in the **stand**
He noticed I was watching him and raised a wrinkled **hand**
He said "Now don't worry lad, about today's big **game**
I helped us win the cup before and I'll do the same **again"**
"We'll score a goal in the second half that I'll put in off the **post"**
It was only then I realized that he was Bertie Fulton's **ghost**
Bertie Fulton was the man who once scored a **goal**
In Britain's 1936 Olympic Team he'd risen from his **hole**
He'd haunt the pitch at Inver Park to give the team some **hope**
Of beating off mighty Celtic who were no foot balling **joke**
As Bertie said they soon slipped up then they came a **cropper**
Bertie smiled at me and said "We'll beat them good and **proper"**.
On ninety minutes the Ref called time I raised my glass in **toast**
It was a lovely treat for me to talk with Bertie's **ghost**
So book your Cup final ticket we have no need to **boast**
There is no doubt that we will win I was told by Bertie's **ghost**

My father was killed in the War in North Africa. I went to Tunisia in 1999 to see his grave but I have also spent time in the Libyan Desert near to where he was wounded. Having been there this first poem of mine sums up my thoughts about the place where my father died.

7903417
Trooper Denis Mc Faul
North Irish Horse
Died Sunday 28th March 1943
Tunisia North Africa

The African Desert

This place is just a barren **land**
With mile after mile of nothing but **sand**
The heat of the sun, and the Flies that **torment**
There were signs of the battles, wherever I **went.**
Other nasty creatures, live in this **land**
Most you wouldn't want, to hold in your **hand**
I saw some Chameleons, funny creatures were **they**
Their eyes sort of swivelled, in a very odd **way**
It's said they change colours I know that they **Do**
I put them on various things, and found it is **true**
The flies were a menace, and buzzed round all **day**
Hundreds of the pests, giving a flying **display**
I had to covered up, to keep the "mosies" at **bay**
My shorts I wore in the daytime, not the end of the **day.**
There was always a risk of Malaria, it was common **enough**
So I took a dose of Perri something, yellow hideous **stuff**
Man's fascination with the desert I find hard to **understand**
I'll never knew why Dad had to go to that God forsaken **land**
The odd Oasis here and the odd well there, hardly a tree to **see**
The Arabs they can have their land I know where I prefer to **be**

When Dad Went to War

I was just a little boy when war it came with tank and **gun**
I never knew if I would see the next rise of the morning **sun**
I was just a lad when told my father died on the **battlefield**
He had served with pride and valour and he did not **yield**
With much pride and dedication of the **NIH** he was **one**
Sent to stop the Nazis and the foe they called the **Hun**
Army Command they decided tank battle must be **done**
The Eight Army won at El Alamein the big push had **begun**
More lives were ended and his memory I can never **shun**
Nor the part he played in the War a war that had to be **won**
It is some time since I found out how dad had met his **fate**
Yet year on year I shed a tear I wish he had been born too **late**
Though he was not quite known to me I am for ever his **one**
It goes without me saying I'm proud to be my father's **son**
But I am sure when got to heaven's gate to Peter he did **say**
One more Trooper reporting Sir I have served my time **today.**

Dad was a Soldier

My dad he left for World War **Two**
To face the Nazis on pastures **new**
A desert country rough with **stones**
With frosty nights that chilled his **bones**
The scorching days to blind his **sight**
A burning Hell until the **night**
He went to keep the peace I **hear**
But all he done was live in **fear**
He stood there in that foreign **land**
Beneath his boots were stones and **sand**
They met upon yon battle **field**
Where all must fight and none must **yield**
Songs of war rang through our **land**
Come on lads lend a fighting **hand**
Seek the enemy and show no **fear**
Dad didn't know his end was **near**
They took his life like a point of **spear**
And took from him all he held **dear**
We all loved him for his tender **heart**
As each and every day he done his **part**
For all this I have four medals **here**
Which were traded for his life I **fear**.

My

Time

in

the

Army

My army career lasted for twenty years which were spent with my wife and children in England, Germany, Northern Ireland, and Cyprus and again in Germany before returning to civilian life in May 1977. I was discharged in the rank of Sergeant. I can honestly say that generally speaking I was happy and I enjoyed my time in the Army. As I look back over the years and realised that our children have been to school in several different places and how it caused my wife and I some concern. Not that the teachers were to blame, more to do with the upheaval of moving every two years and the children getting used to making new friends and the different styles of teaching. I am pleased to say that they managed to get along quite well they can all read and write which is a lot more than can be said for some of the present generation who have had no school interruptions. Two of them are in very senior positions in their Workplace and two have managed to obtain a Degree whilst bringing up their own families. This is a crazy World that we live in today where marriage is treated like a job if you don't like it, leave it. Marriage is not easy, it is like trying to perfect a craft, or a skill, you must work at it accepting that the other person is a human being who has his or her own ways, likes, and dislikes and the secret is to learn to live with what we may see as misgivings, for believe me you don't miss someone until they are gone I know. How I would sum up my Forty plus year old marriage is the "She grew on me". We had our ups and downs like any other couple but I am sure she felt the same as me, we couldn't contemplate being without each other and this was simply because we got to know each other as people. I can't say that people are just getting married too young. I was nineteen and my wife was seventeen. We were both from poor working class families and brought up during the War years. Perhaps it's because we never had much and we didn't expect much, or maybe it's the food that accounts for a divorce rate of one in three that is as good an excuse as any I suppose. I was brought up without a mother or a father from an early age, but it wasn't because my parents couldn't get on with each other.

One might think that after twenty years Military Service and seventy seven years of life that I would have plenty of tales to tell well you would be right I have, but it wouldn't be advisable for me to put most of them in print. Here are just a few.

The Royal Horse Guards

These are not in the order that they occurred but when I was attached to the Royal Horse Guards it was an interesting time as I had the impression that they were in a different Army to the rest of us mere mortals.

We were on an exercise in a wood somewhere in West Germany. The Officer's Mess was practically transported into the exercise area, tablecloths, napkins, cutlery and china, the lot. The servants (as the Royal Horse Guards Officers called them); the rest of the British Army called them batmen, attended to their every need on the exercise. These servants cleaned their long Brown boots each day that were only to be messed up again within a few minutes in the muddy fields. Anyone with half a brain would have been quite content and more comfortable with a pair of Wellington Boots given the circumstances. All I could see was a show of utter contempt tempered with snobbery, towards the people who really do the work on a field exercise. I never could see why they didn't clean their own boots. The rest of us had to and most of all it was the taxpayer's money and time that they were wasting as I fail to see how their clean boots would assist any future War effort as that is what they told us we were training for. I suppose they had a very good use for the Napkins in the event of a Nuclear Strike I should imagine. Or perhaps the Colonel had used his influence to get the Russians to agree not to attack their lovely Mess Tent. If only the Russians had known the truth. Or maybe they did and realised that there was no threat there anyway. On most exercises the younger Officers were happy to eat and "rough" it with the rest of the men.

But in camp we had one Orderly Officer who would visit the cook house on his obligatory tour of the camp at meal times. This pillock would normally ask us; "Wet is the meorl lake" ("What is the meal like".) in our language.

We of course would reply in unison, "It's lovely Sir" to which he would reply;

"Hoy Ged" (Oh Good).

I was at a loss as to how this clown managed on the Parade Square and it must have been great fun on the firing range with him giving the orders.

This one is about the Major who commanded the Squadron that I was attached to with the Royal Horse Guards. He was the biggest twit that I have ever had the misfortune to meet. I used to travel to exercise locations in the leading scout Car as the radio operator was a football team mate. We would lead the way for the convoy to the intended location. On one such occasion we were going through one of the towns in West Germany when some vehicles got detached from the convoy. We decided to get outside the town and regroup instead of holding up the traffic. Our call sign was 18echo. We were stopped at traffic lights when the radio crackled "What is going on 18echo" the voice said. We recognized it as that of the Loony Major (he had read the riot act to me on my first day with the Regiment). Steve, my operator mate told him we were stopped at traffic lights. "The convoy is scattered all over the place" the twit replied. Steve just answered "Ok over" and very quickly the Loony Major said "18echo stay where you are I will take over the lead" Steve again replied "Ok over". It wasn't long until the Major arrived in his Land Rover. He went in front of us and eventually the convoy moved off again. We cleared the town and within a few minutes we could see the rear vehicle with its Green flag, everything was normal, the convoy was together again as we thought it would be once we had got outside the town. We had travelled for quite some distance when Steve said to me "The idiot is going the wrong way". I really didn't know nor did I care, I just didn't want to give him an excuse to blame me for anything that might go wrong. We continued to follow as did the rest of the convoy and then the Major's vehicle signalled to turn left. We were going slightly uphill and turned into a short lane then into a field where we all kept to the hedgerow that led around it. Eventually we came all the way round the field and back to the gate where we had come in. The problem now was that the convoy was still trying to enter the field from the narrow lane. When the major's vehicle reached the gate he couldn't get out even if he wanted to and the remainder of the convey couldn't get into the field so he had to stop and so did the rest of the convoy, most of it inside the field and some of it outside in the lane blocking anyone coming out of the field. We had obviously come to the wrong location as Steve had said before. Soon after we had stopped the radio was alive again. This time the voice said, "18echo this is 01Aplha what is the problem, over?" Steve said to me; "It's the Colonel" and then into his mouth piece. "01Alpha we have been led to the wrong location over". There was a long silence, but the damage had been done. The Colonel obviously thought that we were leading the convoy as usual. Someone had made this cock-up and the Colonel would surely want to know who was responsible. We were only interested that the Colonel and all the rest who would hear the conversations on their radios were aware that we were not guilty, not this time anyway.

This next incident also happened when I was attached to the Royal Horse Guards as a Royal Signals Corporal. One of the duties that we had to perform was Canteen NCO. This duty entailed checking the other ranks bar in the Navy Army Air Force Institution (NAAFI) to ensure that they were all behaving themselves until closing time. Then the Regimental Orderly Corporal would have to secure the premises after checking that all windows were shut, all doors were locked and that the building was free of fire risk from such as smouldering cigarettes or electrical equipment. The worst part of the job was actually getting them all out of the building. Usually there were a few of my sports mates who would make sure that everyone left. This was not such an easy task for one of my fellow Royal Signals Corporals who was called George. Now George was not the sporty type. Nor did he drink very much either. It follows that he didn't get to know very many of the guardsmen and he didn't have friends like mine to assist him. One night when he was on duty George called "Time" and proceeded to check toilets and billiards rooms, locking each in turn when he was satisfied that they had been vacated. Upon his return to the main bar most of the lads had gone, but a few were just finishing off a hand of cards or drinking up. Very soon there were only four soldiers left. George asked them politely to drink up and leave but they didn't take any notice of him. He then told them to leave or they would be on a charge for disobeying a direct order and ask for their names. No one seems to know exactly what happened after this. What we do know is; that when the Orderly Sergeant of the day was making his nightly rounds of the camp he saw that the lights were still on in the NAAFI and it was well past closing time. The Sergeant went to investigate and as he approached the front door he heard someone making a muffled noise. It was George; he had been securely tied up and gagged, then hung up on the peg of one of the toilet doors. There was no one else in sight and believe it or not, the culprits were never caught, I often wondered why, as if I didn't know.

The Orkney Isles

On a much more light hearted note the next incident was much more to my liking. We had arrived in the Orkney Islands from Northern Ireland by Boat, Train and Ferry. All we were told about the military exercise that we were going there for was that it was a survival exercise. Transport included an LCT (Landing Craft Tank) that was to drop us somewhere near The Old Man of Hoy which is 400 feet of rising Sandstone Rock close to the Sea it is a favourite place for rock climbers.

On our second morning we were told to parade outside the HQ Block at 11am in combat dress. After a roll call and a very brief address by the Brigade Major we were marched away to one end of the camp. We were issued with one twenty four hour Compo Ration Pack, a Hexamine Stove, Hexamine tablets, a box of matches, water purifying tablets and the biggest surprise of all, a Live Chicken each. At this point we were told that the exercise would officially start when we boarded the Landing Craft. I was glad to call on my school days experiences of having worked at Armour poultry firm up the Mill Street, killing and plucking chickens to earn a couple of bob after school.. The scenes that followed were like something out of a Dad's Army film. Most of the lads had probably never even seen a live chicken never mind handling one. Soldiers were running everywhere, chasing chickens. Some had used their Lanyard or a piece of string to try and lead their chicken along. I was perfectly aware that chickens don't take kindly to leads. Some were running around Half Plucked, others were almost dead and were jumping and struggling all over the main Barrack Square with their owners trying frantically to pick them up or at best contain them in some way. It was the finest unrehearsed comedy act that I have ever seen. Just think what it might have been like if we had been issued with Geese or even worse, Ganders, instead of Chickens. But in fairness, during our training back at our base we had been SHOWN how to kill a chicken but we hadn't actually practiced it. Likewise we were shown and TOLD how to snare a rabbit but we never actually did it. There was a long delay before everyone was ready to board the Landing Craft to cross to the Old Man of Hoy we had not been given a specific Exercise start time but I can guess that this may well have been because someone anticipated what would happen with the live Chickens.

Catterick Camp.

During my stay at Catterick Camp Wednesdays were always sports afternoons at the Unit where I done my basic military training. There were lists of different sports posted on the notice boards where soldiers put their names on to attend their preferred sport on these afternoons. Sometimes if there was a Regimental Football match in the area, it would be permissible to go to watch the match, as opposed to actually taking part in an activity. But these games were not very often so generally it was to play in the sport of your choice. Everyone paraded on the main Barrack square just before 2pm as a rule. The lists of names were called out and each person was told where to stand as the different sports lists were called. Usually a Corporal from each sports group would be appointed to be in charge of the people who were in that group. He was responsible for making sure that they got to the sports arena on time and that they also took part in the activity, and also that they behaved themselves. The Corporal in charge of the group was given the paper with the list of names for his sport. The place where the event was to take place was always printed at the bottom of the paper. It may be Sandy's Soldiers Home if the sport was swimming, as that was where the swimming baths were located. On one of these afternoons I was in a group that were going to play football. When the officer in charge of the parade read all the names out for those who wanted to play Football, one person was missing. The officer gave the list to the Corporal in charge of our Football group and told him to give the person five minutes to appear or put him on a charge for missing the parade. The problem about where to play football was that though there were many football pitches within Catterick Camp there were also many matches taking place on Wednesday afternoons. It was very important then that the name of the venue was clearly printed at the bottom of the list of names. All the other groups had gone off to their various locations and we were still waiting for our last person to arrive when one of those thick Drill Sergeants happen to come along. Sad to say in those days people, especially Drill Sergeants, were promoted on their ability to stamp their big feet, and shout the loudest. Needless to say they were never considered for training as Tradesmen too much trouble and not enough time for them to pass a course. Soldiers in this category were usually in the Regimental Headquarters Troop and if they were not used as Drill "Pigs" as they were normally referred to as, they were employed on general duties. The general belief was that these people were more apt to get the best out of men by shouting and bullying them into doing what was required of them. These clowns were generally very easily recognised. Big hands big feet and No brains. "What are you lot hanging around for" the Sergeant bellowed as he came striding along the drill square. Our corporal in charge told him what had happened and he asked the Corporal, "Who is missing from the list?" The Corporal replied; "Signalman Henshaw Sergeant"

"Let me see that list" the Sergeant roars, then he looks at our little group of seven or eight people. I can only think that in his haste to let us know that he could count, as well as read, he said "There is another one missing Redpath he is not ticked off on this sheet, charge him as well corporal". If you haven't already guessed Redpath was the name of the Pitch at the bottom of the page, where we had to play our game at that day.

Out of the Mouths of Babes;

I was a Troop Sergeant and my troop commander told me that a certain Lance Corporal was having trouble with one of his sons. The Squadron Commander had asked him to deal with the matter. This Lance corporal had lived next door to me and my family in a block of flats that were our married quarters. I at the time had moved into a house nearer the camp and of course I knew the soldier and his family very well. They had two sons, one was about six years old and the other was about four years old. As I knew the children and their mother I couldn't see it being a serious problem. I told my boss that I would deal with it if he wished and he agreed. After work that day I went to the block of flats and spoke to the two parents. The problem was that the younger of the two sons had thrown a stone at the glass door of the entrance to the block opposite to where they were living. One of the panes of glass got broken. I ask the younger son why he had thrown the stone at the door and he said "They threw one at our door yesterday uncle Dan". The big issue was the fact that it was a civilian block of flats and the German caretaker had to report the incident. When I lived in the tower block I was the "block Senior" and I knew the caretaker fairly well. I assured him that it was an innocent little boy who thought that he had done the right thing and the parents were willing to pay for any repairs. My troop commander saw it in much the same light as I did and the matter ended there, but I had never anticipated having to deal with matters such as these, whilst I was in the Army, I never really seen myself as a social Worker type. But there again, the families were also part of our responsibility and they also came under Military Law; I was learning fast.

The Barrack room Lawyer

Things go wrong from time to time and some people will take advantage of certain situations, that is all part of life wither you are in the Army or out of it. One such case was when the Squadron Sergeant Major asked me to provide a man for a guard duty late one Friday afternoon. A glance at my Wall Chart told me that one of my men was already detailed for the duty that day and I told him that he must have got the wrong troop. The Sergeant Major then told me that the Medical Officer had excused a member of my troop the duty and I would therefore have to provide a replacement for him. This soldier had only recently joined the Regiment. The problem was that he had not informed me that he was excused carrying out the duty. I immediately sent someone to find the soldier and bring him to my office. When I asked the soldier for an explanation he told me that his wife was pregnant and she was afraid to be left by herself at night. My next question was, "How pregnant is your wife" to which he calmly replied, "Six weeks Sergeant". I then asked how long this would last for and he told me. "Until after the baby is born Sergeant". I then asked him why he had not informed me of the Medical Officer's decision as he was detailed for duty that day. His reply was that he forgot. I thought to myself that I had one of those so-called Barrack Room Lawyers. I therefore ask him for his Medical Chit excusing him duties. He replied; "He didn't give me one" so I then said;

"In that case you are excused NOTHING and you had better turn up for your guard duty tonight". Then I said to him;

"Are you excused playing rugby on Friday as well".

I was very surprised when he said, "I don't play Rugby Sergeant".

"Is that so" I said reaching into the top drawer of my desk and taking out a folder then I said "And am I to suppose that this is not your signature here" pointing to the bottom of a form.

He looked at the piece of paper and said;

"Yes that's my signature".

"Good In that case I am charging you with stating a falsehood". I told him; "What falsehood"? He asked. I showed him a form that I had introduced, whereby all newcomers to my troop would fill in a short questionnaire that included the sports that they played. He had listed Rugby as one of his sports and he had signed the document. On the strength of this I had detailed him to play for the troop team. He tried to tell me that there was some mistake so I told him to make his excuses to the Squadron Commander. "He will want to know why you stated that you played Rugby if you don't, unless you were trying to impress someone" I said and before he could reply I went on; "Make no mistake, I will ensure that you get at least seven days Confined to Barracks, you will bring all your kit into camp and you will live in the camp for seven days, who will look after your wife then". He was speechless as his little scam hadn't worked. I gave him the option of being charged as I described or doing five extra duties in addition to the one he was doing that night. He opted for the duties. I then made him go to the Sergeant Major and tell him that he was doing the guard duty that night and that he was volunteering to do an extra five. I was hoping that the Sergeant Major was going to charge him for telling HIM lies, but it seems that he must have thought that I had been hard enough on him. This individual was one of the wasters that we get from time to time; I requested that he be posted to another unit and several weeks later he was posted to Northern Ireland where he could do some more dodging of a different kind.

At another Unit some of my troop members were employed "on loan" to some of the RAF Airfields in West Germany. It was good to get them away from the Regimental routine and it was partially good training in their trade as Royal Signals Linemen. Those who were sent on these exchanges were single men, or married unaccompanied soldiers. The main thing was that they were Volunteers. One day I received a phone call from one of the RAF Officers at RAF Gutterslough. He very briefly told me that one of my men one of the married ones, was being held in the Guardroom. I arranged that two escorts and I would pick the soldier up that afternoon and bring him back to the Regiment. The story was that the soldier had been drinking in the Other Rank's bar and refused to leave when the Duty Officer told him to. He was drunk and he had told the Officer that he could not tell him what to do as he was in the Army, not the RAF. The Officer told the soldier to go to bed and "sleep it off". The soldier then got very aggressive and started to throw some of the furniture about. The officer contacted the Guardroom and had him arrested. Between the time of contacting the Guardroom and the RAF Police arriving at the scene, the soldier had broken a mirror and quite a few glasses. The escorts and I brought him back to the Regiment and he was charged with "Conduct prejudice to the order of good military discipline" or something like that and also malicious damage. He elected to be dealt with by the Commanding Officer and he was given a sentence of five days detention and ordered to pay the cost of the damage incurred. I was glad to get this incident out of the way. But unfortunately it was not to be as the soldier's wife came to see me the following morning. When she came to my office I ask her to take a seat and asked how I could help her. She told me that she had been to the Guardroom and that she had been refused permission to see her husband. I tried to explain that I was in no position to interfere and that if she wished I would get the Squadron Commander to speak to her as he may be able to help. I had also told her that her husband was under detention and basically no one was allowed to speak to him. "But I'm his wife" she said between sobs. She then told me that I was to blame for him "Being put in jail". I reminded her that it wasn't me who tried to wreck the other ranks bar at RAF Gutterslough but she said that if I hadn't sent him there in the first place this wouldn't have happened. I told her that her husband had volunteered to go to the airfield and that it was to give him more help to advance in his trade. She then told me that I was telling a pack of lies as her husband had said that he had to go as it was an order. The light began to dawn as far as I was concerned. Her husband fancied a few days away with the other lads boozing at night times so he told his wife that he had been ordered to go to the airfield. By this time the lady was crying with tears running down her face. She then stood up and said, "You got him into this mess so you can look after his children" and she left the Office closing the door behind her and leaving the two children with me. This time I wished that I had been trained as a Social worker at least I might have known what to do about the children.

I was seen as the "villain of the peace" in this case when one of my corporals went to Catterick Camp from West Germany on an upgrading course. As was our routine, a day or so after he went on his course my boss (a Captain) and I visited the Corporal's wife to make sure that she had no serious problems while her husband was away for something like eight weeks.

We left the wife in the knowledge that should she encounter any problems that she should contact me in the first instance and the military would sort out the problem if it was beyond my powers. All was fine until three weeks after my boss and I had spoken to the wife. The Troop Sergeant from the next Troop Office to mine came to inquire if I knew that the Corporal's wife had no money. "I have no idea" I told my fellow Sergeant who lived in the same block of flats as the Corporal and his wife were living.

It seems that she had not received any money from her husband nor had she received any personal mail from him. I told the Sergeant that I would take the matter from here and thanked him for letting me know about it.

My first "port of call" was the Regimental Pay Office as the procedure was that when personnel were leaving families behind for more than two weeks the soldier would arrange that a portion of his salary is paid through the Regimental Pay office, on a weekly basis to the wife.

The Pay Office was unaware that the Corporal had made no provision to pay his wife any money. The pay Corporal did however ring the training unit at Catterick Camp and ascertained that the Corporal was paid in Catterick. In the meantime I was asked to go and see the Squadron 2IC and he wanted to know why the Corporal's wife had no money to feed herself and her children. "It is part of your job Sergeant to make sure that this sort of thing doesn't happen" he told me in no uncertain terms.

Before I could tell him anything he said "Go and sort it Sergeant and report to me when it is". He was a great help as usual. I then went to the post Corporal to find out about the Corporal's wife and her personal mail. I could not believe what I was hearing from this Post corporal. He and the wife's husband were both Geordies from Sunderland and were very good friends. The Corporal on the course had made arrangements to be paid his full amount of wage and he decided to send the wife her housekeeping money by Money Order through the post. At the same time the Post Corporal had been requested to send ALL the mail to the Corporal on the course to him at Catterick Camp.

Consequently the weekly money orders were being sent from Cattrick Camp by the husband and promptly returned to him as was the wife's personal mail by the Post Corporal.

I can tell you that after this escapade I was looking forward to the Corporal getting back from his course and doing his annual assessment.

It was not all problems being a troop Sergeant as I was very amused one afternoon when I visited the Regimental Headquarters building to see the Chief Clerk. It happened to be a day when a General was visiting the camp. I had just entered the building and was walking along one of the corridors when a Sergeant from the Education Corps emerged from one of the offices. He was not wearing any headdress as he worked in the building, He was wearing thick horn rimmed glasses and he was carrying a pile of books which necessitated him using both hands and arms. Before the Sergeant got to me, the General and his escorts came out of one of the other offices. The entourage turned to proceed in the direction of the Sergeant who must have wondered how he was going to salute the General as he passed him, because he stopped and stood with his back against the wall to enable the party to get past him. When the time came, the Sergeant stood to attention and bowed his head in salute, as the General passed him. By this time I was just slightly behind the General's party and I heard the Quartermaster (who was an Irishman) say to the General, "Take no notice of him Sur, he's a Buddhist".

When I was researching a book that I wrote on our family history I had a dream about my father and my mother. It inspired me to write this nice little story to the memory of my parents.

I Had a Dream

It had been a long trying day for me, but at last I was home again. The rail journey from Belfast had been the worst that I could ever remember. It was stop and start all the way with one delay after the other and precious little of anything to eat or drink on the train. Then there was the breakdown when trying to leave the platform at Carrickfergus. All the passengers had to get off while they found another train. There was also talk about ferrying the travellers to their various destinations by Bus. Three and a half hours to travel twenty five miles on what was supposed to be a modern train. But at least I had found the birthday present that I wanted for my dear wife Margaret and I had already phoned her to tell her of the delay until 7.30pm (she was under the impression that I had gone to a football match). Margaret said that she would be waiting in the car park for me at the Town Station. I would now soon be home for supper and a relaxing evening in front of the Television. I wouldn't describe myself as one of life's high flyers, I was perfectly happy to draw a month's pay for a fairly routine job that I was happy doing. Margaret and I would have liked a little more in the way of life's comforts, but we were not really struggling to make ends meet, not now that the children were off our hands. We had a little money left over at the end of each month these days, instead of the other way round. At 60 years of age, I had to retire, according to company policy. It was really to save them money. Tomorrow was my wife's birthday Friday 13th September 2008. I had noticed the weather closing in as the journey continued to Larne where we lived at number 16 Mill Lane. The fog was ever thickening as I eventually stood in the Station at Larne watching the train pull out from the long platform number 1 on its way to the last stop at Larne Harbour. Visibility was down to about ten yards, I couldn't even see the Glar-beds. I looked around at the now dark and deserted platform and wondered why I had been the only passenger to alight from the train. At first I wondered if I had got off at the wrong station because the surroundings seemed to somehow look different. But at the same time they were vaguely familiar. It wasn't until I approached the exit from the Station that I saw the name plate LARNE. This was definitely the correct place but I felt an eerie unease creeping through my body as I realised that I was standing on the platform of the Larne Station that had closed in 1965; and then demolished the following year. I thought to myself, "I should know this place, I worked here as a porter, a guard and a Shunter way back in the early 1950s, but how could this be"? As the fog started to lift, the immediate area became clearer and to my amazement the Market Place outside the station to my left had disappeared and was replaced by the Regal Cinema which had closed its doors for the last time in 1961. By this time, I was now pretty sure of where I was, the only question was, what year was this? I was thinking that I needed to find a shop or something familiar and if memory served me right there used to be a Fish and Chip shop on the right, at the top of Station Road, near the corner with Bridge Street. I looked at my watch the time was 7.35 pm just five minutes after the time that I should have been meeting my wife Margaret. (She would be waiting for me in the car park). But of course there was no car park there. I walked up Station Road, turned into Bridge Street, over the bridge and realization appeared, there it was the Thatch pub. Across the road was Dan Campbell's Store, with the usual array of advertising boards and stuff hanging on racks outside the shop. I couldn't resist having a peek up Mill Street and I recognized The Mourne Clothing Company building. But what I really needed was a newspaper and a fresh packet of cigarettes. I walked down Dunluce Street and into the Larne Times Newspaper shop, next door to their Office. The doorbell tinkled as I entered and an elderly man came through from the back room. The man smiled and asked if he could be of help. I asked him for a newspaper and twenty Superking cigarettes. The man looked at me as if I was mad. "What?" he said. "A newspaper and twenty Superking cigarettes please", I repeated. "We've got Park Drive, Woodbines, or Gallagher Blue, take your pick". I opted for the Woodbines, then fiddled around amongst the change in my pocket and selected a couple of twenty pence pieces and passed them to the shopkeeper who picked up the coins and looked at them. He glanced back at me and said; "What's this?" "What's what?" I said. "This" the man said, holding the coins up in front of my face. "Oh, I'm sorry" I replied fumbling in my pocket for some more money. "Daft twit, you've given me too much. What price are fags where you come from?" He handed back to me, one of the twenty pence pieces together with the change from the other one. I heaved a sigh of relief and apologised again. The shopkeeper smiled and slowly shook his head. I looked at my watch again, 7.45 pm and still a little shaken I left the shop and looked at the top of the newspaper. The date was Thursday 25th of March 1947, just two years after the end of World War Two in Europe. My first thoughts were about how I am going to get back to 2008. Margaret would be at the station waiting for me and wondering where I had got to after the train departed. But where on Earth can I go for help. I had to think fast. Then I had a brainwave; Quay Lane of course if this was really 1947 then my Grandparents would be living in Quay Lane with my father and it was only a ten minute walk away. There was no time to lose and at least it would give me time to think as I walked and to work out what my next move was going to be. This would need some thought. I could pass myself off as a relative, if they asked me questions, because my dad had told me stories of life at Quay Lane. Stories like when Granddad and his brothers were able to take their fishing boat out into Larne Lough from the back yard when the tide was right. My Grandfather Daniel McFaul was regarded locally as something of a 'free spirit' and he was easily identified by his Hitler moustache. He would, in later years, be regarded by some as a bit of an odd ball. Still, that didn't make me feel any easier as I walked up the street and knocked on the old "Property Brown" coloured front door of number 4 Quay Lane. A blonde woman in her thirties opened it, and it was all I could do to prevent myself wrapping my arms around her. This was my aunt Sarah Alice, my father's sister and if I had a favourite, she was it. "I'm sorry to bother you" I said "But could I speak to Denis McFaul, please?" I was asked to wait for a moment, and after a brief conversation inside, a man in his sixties appeared at the door. I had only ever seen photographs of my grandfather before and it was now rather strange and emotional to meet him face to face. I knew it was my Grandfather as he still had that Hitler moustache He had an air of dignity about him but working as a docker at Larne Harbour all his life, had clearly taken its toll. I explained to him that I was a relative and that I was trying to trace Denis McFaul as I had something to give to him. If this conversation had taken place in 2008 the door would probably have been shut in my face, but back in 1947 people were inclined to be more trusting towards strangers after the upheaval of the war and the displacement of large numbers of the population. I was invited inside and offered refreshments when I explained that I had come all the way from Belfast. The house was as I remembered it when I had been there with my Grandmother, when my Grandfather was at work. I felt strangely out of place even in these familiar and yet somehow strange surroundings. I recognised the old Grandfather clock against the wall, except it wasn't so old, the time was 7.55pm. My Grandfather gave me a slip of paper with an address on it, and told me that his son Denis had been married for several years and was living at that address with his wife, Mary Ellen. I breathed a huge sigh of relief as I realised that I had not yet been born. What would have happened if I had bumped into myself? I dared not think about it. I gratefully accepted the cup of tea offered to me and smiled as I saw the Organ in the corner, an old friend from past years. My Grandmother used to let me bang on the keyboard to keep me out of mischief. Grandfather noticed my glance. "Do you play the organ?" he said. "Not for many years, would you mind if I tried?" I ask. "Not at all" said my Grandfather. "There's some sheet music in the stool seat". I spent a further quarter of an hour with the old Organ and found all the old times coming back to me. I finished my second cup of tea and prepared to leave. It was nearly 9.00pm and it would take me about fifteen minutes to get to my father's address. I managed to gloss over one or two of my Grandfather's probing questions about my connection to the family. I thanked my Grandfather for his hospitality and set out for my father's house. My main priority was getting back home in the correct year and a plan was developing in my brain. This was 1947 and I was the possessor of a considerable amount of information not available to anyone in this time. I wondered about the possibility of maybe just persuading my father to have a bet on the horses, or the Football Pools or maybe the FA Cup Final. My father Denis McFaul had never, to the best of my knowledge, been a betting man, apart from the usual small weekly flutter on the football pools. Of course, that was it. I couldn't possibly remember or predict enough draws to enable my father to hit the jackpot with Littlewoods or any of the other operators, but my sporting knowledge is quite good and I did know the result of the FA Cup Final that was taking place in 32 days' time between Charlton Athletic and Burnley. I was also pretty sure that I knew the winner of the Grand National which was taking place in 4 days' time on Saturday March 29th 1947. The Winner CAUGHOO won at 100/1. I stopped at the War Memorial outside the Laharna Hotel and sat down on the step there. Taking a piece of paper from my wallet and a pen from my top pocket, I wrote the information down, ready to hand over to my father. I was now ready for another strange encounter as I knocked at a very familiar door, number 19 Ronald Street where I was born. It was opened by my father. I explained that I had travelled from Belfast and that I had some important information which he must not give to anyone else. We went into the back parlour where the list was produced and instructions given for its use. Denis, unlike his father, was suspicious and asked what the catch was. "No catch, I told him, just put any winnings into a building society. Keep the book somewhere safe, like under a loose floor board on the stairs, and don't tell anyone where it is." My father looked at me brow furrowed, but took the piece of paper and after giving it a cursory glance put it in his pocket. As far as I was concerned, only time would tell now; and I really had to leave. I made my excuses, saying that I had a train to catch and left. At the end of Ronald Street I turned around and saw my dad standing under the street lamp close to the house watching me. It was now 10.00pm and very soon I was hurrying past the Thatch Pub in Bridge Street on my way back to the station only to find it closed for the night. I had figured that as the station had 'brought' me to 1947, maybe catching a train there would take me back to 2008. It seemed the only chance I would have, but now there was the need for somewhere to sleep for the night. I decided to use the Laharna Hotel. I had a little money from the change given to me by the newsagent, but had no other money with me. I decided to face that problem when it arose. The Hotel was not too expensive and I could also get a meal. It seemed ages since I had eaten and I felt as though time had stood still. I explained to the manager of the Hotel about my financial position and he said that my Seiko watch would suffice as full payment. People were inclined to barter in those days when money was in short supply. The accommodation was comfortable and shortly after dinner I retired to bed and was soon sound asleep. A knock at the bedroom door the following morning confirmed to me that it had not all been a dream and I went down to a full breakfast. I was now nearer to Larne Harbour Station so I decided to get the train from there to the town station where Margaret was to meet me. The Station Master at the Harbour was just arriving as I approached the ticket office and I accepted the offer of a cup of tea while I waited for the early morning train to depart. Getting into the first carriage I thought that I would simply travel back up the line and get off at the first stop. Looking out of the window I noticed that a dense fog had started to form again as the train passed the Glarbeds and the sky had become very dark. This was nothing new for Larne Harbour, where the wind frequently reached gale force and the mist came in from the sea. The train halted at the first stop Larne; and like before, I was the only passenger to alight, it wasn't until the carriages had cleared the platform that I recognised where I was. I was back at the modern station at 7.35pm and presumably in 2008. I stood for a moment as the fog cleared and I was diverted from my thoughts by the tooting of a car horn. Turning around I was relieved to see Margaret waving at me from the car park. I tried to explain to her what had happened and asked if she had been worried that I hadn't been on the platform the previous day. She gave me an odd kind of look and asked me what day I thought it was. There had been no loss in time whilst I had "been in 1947" and nothing unusual had happened. However, when I saw an entry in the Properties section of the Larne Times some weeks later, my interest was awakened. My parent's old home in Ronald Street was up for sale. They had died some years earlier and the council had sold the property to a private purchaser. But this person had now moved on, leaving the house vacant and in the hands of a local estate agent. A telephone call got me the keys to the house and an uninterrupted viewing. This was my chance to see if my dad had carried out the scheme which I had suggested. Taking a few tools along in a carrier bag, I set off. There was no one about when I got there towards lunchtime, and letting myself in I made for the stairs. Thinking back to my childhood I remembered that the stair riser next to the top had always been loose and dad had never got around to fixing it. Taking a screwdriver out of the bag I levered it to one side to find a brown envelope behind it. With trembling hands I opened it and a building society deposit book fell out. I took a deep breath, opened it at the last page and sat back in amazement. The date of the last deposit was listed as 1971 and the balance stood at £754, 254 and 65 pence. This was the inheritance; and since I was the only child left it was mine. It wasn't until my head had cleared and my eyes refocused, that I saw a little stamp at the bottom of the page:

Account Closed - 26th May 1972

There was a neatly folded piece of notepaper on the stair and this had clearly fallen out of the book when I opened it. I unfolded it and immediately recognised my mother's handwriting. My mother's message to my father was brief and to the point;

25 May 1972

Dear Denis,

Thanks for the gift. I'll make sure that I find a good use for it after all the years that I have spent penny pinching with you. Don't bother looking for me I will be long gone by the time you read this.

      Mary Ellen.

I had to smile, when I woke up, you see, in 'real life' mum and dad had stayed happily together, but evidently my actions in 1947 had completely changed the whole course of our McFaul family history. Now I know why I have so much trouble trying to trace people for my Family Tree.

A Final Thought

My motivation to write this brief account of my ramblings is because I am fed up listening to this pampered present day generation moaning and groaning about what has not yet been provided free for them. If it is not expecting the tax payer to foot the bill for THEIR children's school uniforms, it's about telling the world how badly they have been treated by the State despite the fact that they haven't worked for years and don't appear to want to. Yet they run a Car, go to the pub every weekend, have holidays abroad and smoke 20 plus Cigarettes every day. They also have Mobile phones, Televisions, Washing Machines, Dish Washers, Fridge and Computer with broadband, not to mention Membership of their local Golf Club. This applies to a few people that spring to my mind and there are more like them.

One chap is 35 years old and has worked on and off for only ten of those years. This chap will never grace the workplace with his presence again. He doesn't want to he is much better off with all the benefits that he gets today, including the one for his bad back, which is under considerably strain as you can imagine and sympathise with, every time he hit's a golf ball a couple of hundred yards down the fairways. He really earns his benefit money through his suffering. No doubt he will pass down to his descendants the skills that he acquired in the art of workless survival. My thanks for surviving so long are not due to the Chancellor of the Exchequer, or to the vast array of Government hand outs that are available to these lazy idle people. I find it hard to sympathise when someone that is getting six weeks off work because they are "stressed". Some even have to take early retirement because of stress. Who invented the silly word anyway probably one of those that I have been talking about. I have often wondered how they would have fared in the War with bombs raining down on them. Or like my mother and many other mothers who were wondering where the next meal was coming from to feed their families. I personally am grateful to the **Overdrawn** Department of the National Westminster Bank, Visa Card and my Car and Mortgage Insurance companies for encouraging me to keep working, by sending me their never ending letters and threats of repossession. I couldn't have lasted for 44 years in the workforce otherwise. I relied on those letters to make me carry on working and I couldn't have survived without the stress of receiving them.

Dear Aunt Sarah

You know as I sit here thinking recalling all the **years**
I just remember the good times I forget the pain and **tears**
I remember all the good things our house and all the **love**
The time we lived together and I thank my stars **above**
I now live in a different world indeed another **era**
The credit for her part in this is down to dear Aunt **Sarah**
It's nice to sit and think like this as an old yin I **declare**
The yarns I've told you are all true believe me I was **there.**

182